WORLD WAR II
TANKS

The Axis Powers: Germany, Italy and Japan

by Eric Grove

Special illustrations by the County Studio, Coleorton, Leicester

CONTENTS

GERMANY

Despite their lack of interest in armoured operations during World War I, German views changed in succeeding years. With an army reduced to 100,000 men by the Treaty of Versailles, a favourable climate was created for soldiers like Heinz Guderian to find ways of substituting technology for manpower. Versailles also forbade the Germans any tanks, and development had to be carried out in secret in Sweden and Russia as well as Germany itself. Inspired by the writings of British progressives, such as Colonel Fuller, the idea of an armoured division – a combined 'all arms' formation based around brigades of tanks and moving at their speed – began to evolve. In 1931, Guderian was appointed Chief of Staff to the Inspectorate of Motorized Troops and the stage was set for the organization of a modern German armoured force. Planning began for new light and medium tanks which eventually became the *PzKpfw* III and IV but for short term training lighter *PzKpfw* I and II – originally designated agricultural tractors to disguise their true purpose – were decided upon.

With the election of Hitler as Chancellor in 1933, German armour gained a powerful advocate, and two years later with the renunciation of the Versailles Treaty open re-armament began. The Motorized Troops Command became the Armoured Troops Command and three *Panzer* (armoured) divisions were formed,

the second under Guderian himself. Each had an establishment of a tank brigade (562 tanks, later reduced to 276–324), a reconnaissance battalion, infantry brigade, field artillery regiment and other support units, all motorized.

Everything did not immediately go Guderian's way. The Fourth Tank Brigade was set up as an infantry support formation and the cavalry formed four Light Divisions each with a single light tank battalion for screening duties. However, the occupation of Austria in 1938 illustrated not only the mechanical weaknesses of the new German tanks but also the advantages of their remarkable long-range mobility – Second Panzer Division of Guderian's Corps covered 420 miles (675·78 kilometres) in 48 hours. With this vindication of their utility two more *Panzer* divisions were formed, the Fourth and Fifth. Hitler himself assumed personal charge of the armed forces and appointed Guderian head of Mobile Troops.

The first full scale demonstration of blitzkrieg warfare in 1939 was more than enough to overwhelm Poland, although, due to delays in development, the majority of the tanks used were *PzKpfw* Is and IIs. After this victory in the East the four Light divisions were up-graded to full *Panzer* status (up to 218–29 tanks).

Shortages remained, however, and when Germany invaded France and the Low Countries, out of a total of 2,574 tanks over half were still

PzKpfw Is and IIs. Most of the available heavier German armour was concentrated in the hands of the three *Panzer* divisions of Guderian's XIX *Panzer* Corps, which, together with two mainly Czech equipped *Panzer* divisions of XLI *Panzer* Corps, made the decisive breakthrough around Sedan and drove to the Channel coast by the end of the month. Armoured warfare, properly conducted over short distances and in relatively easy terrain *could* humble a more conventional army; the doubts of the German High Command, which had almost succeeded in holding back the progress of the race across France, were stilled and the number of *Panzer* divisions was ordered to be doubled.

Armour appeared to offer victories that were cheap in industrial and economic resources as well as lives and time. The output of the apparently mighty German war machine remained limited and tank production during 1940 was only 1,460 – an increase over the previous year's 249 but hardly enough for requirements. If more divisions were needed available tank strength would have to be spread more widely and the tank component of the *Panzer* division was lowered to one regiment of 150–200 vehicles.

In February 1941 an *ad hoc* group of elements of Third *Panzer* Division was sent to Africa as the Fifth Light Division; this was followed by a full *Panzer* division, the Fifteenth, in April and these two formed *Deutsche Afrika Korps*

whose exploits under Rommel again demonstrated German expertise in armoured warfare. In September 1941 Fifth Light became Twenty-first *Panzer* Division and *DAK* the *Panzergruppe Afrika*. In 1942 Rommel's whole Axis army became *Panzerarmee Afrika* for the final push on Egypt that ended at Alamein.

By then, events in this theatre, were overshadowed by those elsewhere. With their French experience the German army was confident of quick victory against Hitler's major target, Russia. Over 3,200 tanks were committed in the initial onslaught in 17 *Panzer* divisions.

But over much greater distances and against individually superior Soviet tanks the weapon that had crushed France proved inadequate. As the *Panzer* divisions pushed deeper into Western Russia so the logistical problems became more and more difficult. Winter made the situation even worse and the bid for a lightning victory finally stalled at the gates of Moscow. Recriminations followed, and Guderian was reduced to the reserve.

Tank production was increased for a renewed offensive in 1942 but there were still insufficient vehicles for all the *Panzer* divisions which now numbered 25; only those formation which spearheaded the attack in the south were fully equipped, each with three battalions of *PzKpfw* III and IV, about 170 tanks. This could only be done by stripping the formations on other parts of the front and these were reduced to one or two understrength tank battalions. These redeployments were rewarded by more massive tactical victories in the 1942 summer offensive but as the focus shifted from the Caucasus to Stalingrad so the stage was set for disaster. By the end of January 1943 an entire German army had been forced to surrender at Stalingrad.

With the total available German tank strength down to only 27 tanks per division, Guderian was recalled as Inspector General of Armoured Troops with wide powers to put Germany's armoured forces back on their feet. It was only now, after her first major defeat, that the German economy was fully mobilized for war. By 1944 Guderian planned to have all the *Panzer* divisions on a four tank battalion basis, 400 tanks in all.

Despite all efforts – 12,151 AFVs being constructed in 1943, half of which were tanks – this was an impossible target to achieve. In addition, the major German offensive of 1943, the assault against the Kursk salient, was stopped dead in its tracks after some of the heaviest armoured battles of all time, with equally large-scale casualties. German problems were not helped either by arguments over the control of vehicles and by the creation of new *élite* formations, such as the Nazi Party's own army the *Waffen SS*, which got priority in the allocation of equipment. The average *Panzer* division had only two tank battalions, one of *PzKpfw* IVs and one of *Panther* tanks, each composed of a total of four 17–22 tank companies.

When the Western Allies opened the second front in the west, the German forces were caught between two well-equipped opponents. Despite the largest production figures yet – 8,328 tanks and 10,659 other armoured fighting vehicles being produced in 1944 to 1945 – and also flashes of the old skill in armoured operations on both fronts, the Germans were finally overwhelmed by superior resources and the Allies' command of the air.

Between 1939 and 1945 the Germans produced some 23,500 tanks and 17,445 other armoured fighting vehicles, the majority after 1942. These were impressive figures but do not compare well with other major combatants' production. The Germans were unprepared for the length of the war they had begun and they mobilized their industries too late. Nor did they help themselves by their passion for technological improvement and plans for new vehicles, often highly impractical, which delayed and complicated production. Strategic insight and, latterly, technological superiority could be significant and sometimes decisive but they could not overcome administrative and managerial failures.

Left: Three of the five 'Neubaufahrzeug' experimental multi-turreted heavy tanks built in 1934–5

PzKpfw I and II

The *PzKpfw* I and II – originally designed as stop-gap, light, training tanks – formed the backbone of the German *Panzer* forces until well after the beginning of World War II. The *PzKpfw* I dated back to 1932 when a specification for a simple tank, to train the new armoured divisions, was issued to MAN, Krupp, Daimler Benz and Rheinmetall Borsig. Krupp, using knowledge gained in Sweden and from a Carden Loyd tankette, produced an *LKA* chassis with four coil-sprung road wheels each side and a trailing idler touching the ground. A rear-mounted, 57-hp, Krupp M305 petrol engine drove through the front sprockets. This two-man vehicle mounting two 7·9-mm MG 13 machine-guns in a small turret on the right-hand side was chosen for production, with Daimler Benz superstructure, under the pseudonym *Landwirtschaftschlepper* (*LaS*) – agricultural tractor – to disguise its intended purpose.

Production began in 1934 on an initial order for 150 chassis with smaller wheels and an external girder each side to carry the leaf-spring suspension of the rear three wheels and idler. Troop trials showed that the new tank was underpowered and the IB *LaS* May was developed with a new larger 100-bhp Maybach NL 38 TR engine. This improved the tank's power to weight ratio and ability to cover difficult ground but the already disappointing range of 91 miles (146 km) was reduced slightly to 87 miles (140 km). Weight was also increased and length from 13 feet 2 inches to 14 feet 7 inches (4·02 m to 4·42 m). Height remained 5 feet 8 inches (1·72 m), width 6 feet 10 inches (2·06 m) and armour was also unchanged at 13 mm maximum, enough to protect against small-arms fire only. The new engine necessitated a lengthened suspension with five wheels and a raised idler.

In 1935, with open rearmament, the need for subterfuge disappeared and the two tanks became *Panzerkampfwagen* I (MG) *Ausführung* A and B; about 300 and 1,500 respectively were built. Despite their lack of firepower and protection, due to delays in the development of the *PzKpfw* III and IV production continued until 1941; while at the outbreak of war they constituted over a third of Germany's tank force.

Many fought in Poland in 1939 and they also appeared in Norway and Denmark the next year. In the French campaign 523 were still on the strength of the *Panzer* divisions where good logistics made up for deficiencies in range. As

late as the invasion of Russia and the campaign in the Western Desert *PzKpfw* I *Ausf* A and B were still in first-line service although by the end of 1941 most were relegated to their original training roles or had been converted.

Between 1936 to 1938, 200 *PzKkfw* Is (mostly *Ausf* B) were converted to *Kleiner Panzerbefehls-wagen* (small armoured command vehicles) *SdKfz* 265. These had a high, fixed, 30-mm armoured superstructure, mounting a single machine-gun, and extra radio equipment for control of armoured operations – a vital component of the blitzkrieg concept. Ninety were with the *Panzer* divisions that moved on France in May 1940.

In order to provide mobile artillery for the *Panzer* and motorized divisions the *PzKpfw* I *Ausf* B chassis was used for two pioneer self-propelled guns, both developed in 1939 by Alkett of Berlin. One carried the 47-mm Czech *PaK* 36 (*t*) anti-tank gun in a small, three-sided open mount. A total of 132 were on strength

by July 1941 and the type saw service in tank destroyer battalions in both Russia and North Africa. The other modification was a large 150-mm heavy infantry gun (*sIG* 33) in a massive three-sided 10-mm armoured box on the front of the chassis; 38 of these clumsy vehicles were produced and they provided direct gunfire support for motorized infantry in the Polish, French and Russian campaigns.

An attempt was made to convert the *PzKpfw* I into an eight-ton *Ausf* C fast reconnaissance vehicle but only one *VK* 301 prototype was built. Another, much heavier (18-ton) modification, *Ausf* D (*VK* 1801) with 80-mm armour and a heavy interleaved suspension was developed for infantry purposes in the summer of 1940. With its two machine-gun armament and a speed of only 15 mph (24 km/h), this design – an aberration in German armoured ideas – reflected the continued power of the traditional arms although only 30 were built out of a total order for 130 tanks.

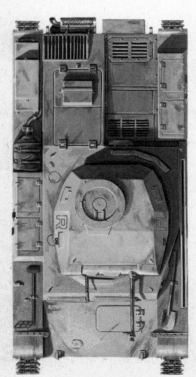

PzKpfw II Ausf F
Weight 9.35 tons (9.5 tonnes)
Crew three
Armament one 20-mm KwK 30 gun with 180 rounds and one 7.92-mm MG 34 machine-gun with 2,550 rounds
Armour hull nose 35 mm, driver's plate 30 mm, sides 20 mm, decking 10 mm, belly 5 mm, tail 15 mm; turret front 30 mm, sides 20 mm, rear 15 mm, top 10 mm
Engine one Maybach HL 62 TR inline six-cylinder liquid-cooled petrol, 140-hp
Speed 25 mph (40 km/h)
Range 118 miles (190 km)
Trench crossing 5 feet 7 inches (1.7 m)
Vertical step 1 foot 4½ inches (42 cm)
Fording 3 feet (90 cm)
Length 15 feet 9 inches (4.81 m)
Width 7 feet 6 inches (2.28 m)
Height 6 feet 8 inches (2.02 m)

Left: *A PzKpfw Ausf F captured from 10th Panzer division in Tunisia. It is painted sand yellow and the turret markings are those of a headquarters vehicle of one of the division's Panzer regiments. A Panzer regiment HQ had up to five such reconnaissance tanks. Note the Ausf F recognition features: the wide full-length driver's plate with dummy right-hand aluminium visor to confuse hostile gunners searching for a vulnerable spot, the conical rear idlers and the lack of turret stowage bin*

The *PzKpfw* II dated back to 1934 when a specification was issued for an improved light tank to fill the gap caused by the delay in development of heavier vehicles. Krupp offered an *LKA* II prototype based on their previous tank but this time the MAN offering was chosen. This new *LaS* 100 chassis had six small road wheels each side, sprung in pairs between the sides of the tank and an outside girder. A 130-hp Maybach engine drove the seven-ton vehicle via the front sprocket. The driver steered using the normal clutch and brake system as on the earlier *LaS*. A turret mounting a 20-mm *KwK* 30 automatic gun, together with an *MG* 34 machine-gun was fitted and maximum armour thickness was 14·5 mm. For this period the 20-mm weapon had an acceptable armour piercing performance: 24 mm of vertical armour at 500 yards (457 m).

Limited production began in 1935 and the first 25 1/*LaS* 100s entered service as the *PzKpfw* II (2 cm) *Ausf* a1 (*SdKfz* 121). A further 25 a2 and 50 a3 followed with minor improvements to engine and suspension. A new larger (140-hp) engine was fitted to the next 100 *Ausf* bs with 30-mm armour which increased weight to nearly eight tons. With the next limited pre-production series, *Ausf* c, a new suspension of five medium-sized, elliptically-sprung road wheels was adopted which became standard for the remainder of the series. With larger tanks still in short supply, full-scale production began in 1937 by MAN, Famo, MIAG and later Wegmann. The first production model was the *Ausf* A which had a new, angular, welded nose instead of the previous rounded casting and this was followed by the *Ausf* B and C with turret cupolas instead of periscopes for commander's observation.

In 1939 there were 1,226 *PzKpfw* IIs of all types in service, although by this time the deficiencies of the tank in armour and firepower had already become clear – the armour was not thick enough to withstand modern anti-tank guns and, perhaps more important, the 20-mm gun was becoming increasingly useless against more modern tanks. Nevertheless, the

Opposite page: *An example of the last PzKpfw II model to see service, albeit in small quantities, the Ausf L 'Luchs' (Lynx) reconnaissance tank. This photograph shows one of the tanks of a Waffen SS reconnaissance unit captured in France*
Above: *In the first winter on the Russian front PzKpfw II and III were still operating together as main battle tanks. The interesting PzKpfw II Ausf F on the right, appears to have had its puny 20-mm gun replaced with a more powerful weapon, possibly a captured French 37-mm SA-38. The cupola is also modified*
Below: *Another use for the PzKpfw II chassis was as a carriage for the 150-mm sIG 33 heavy infantry gun. This example is seen knocked out in the Western Desert*

PzKpfw II proved adequate in Poland and even in France as the major single type (950 tanks) in the *Panzer* Divisions that struck on 10 May. As with the *PzKpfw* I strategic and tactical prowess made up for technical deficiencies.

This initial success perhaps distorted the perspective of the High Command, which kept the *PzKpfw* II in production although only 15 had been built in 1939 and 9 in 1940, 233 appeared in 1941. These were of a new version, *Ausf* F, with redesigned frontal plating up-armoured to 30·36 mm, but speed was reduced by 10 mph (16 km/h) due to the extra weight. A few had a new 20-mm gun, the lengthened *KwK* 38. Two more similar types, *Ausf* G and J appeared with the addition of a storage-bin to the turret. All these later models had a new, conical rear idler. Over 1,060 *PzKpfw* IIs were available for action during the opening weeks of the invasion of Russia but over such vast distances, and against a more heavily armed and armoured enemy, the weaknesses of the design were even more apparent. In order to make good the vehicle's deficiencies a few *PzKpfw* IIs received new armament, some being fitted with what appears from photographic evidence to be a French 37-mm *SA* 38. By April of the next year the number in action had slumped to 866 despite continued production, and increasingly they were relegated to reconnaissance duties.

From 1942, large numbers of *Ausf* A, B, C and F chassis were used as the basis for self-propelled guns armed with the new 75-mm *PaK* 40/2 which could penetrate the latest Soviet armour. These *Panzerjägers* were designated *Marder* II (*SdKfz* 131). During 1942 and 1943 531 were converted and issued to the tank destroyer battalions of *Panzer* and infantry divisions. The most numerous SP on the standard *PzKpfw* II chassis was the *Wespe* (Wasp – *SdKfz* 124) with a 105-mm *FH* 18/2 field howitzer, with muzzle brake, which was mounted in a high

Wespe
Weight 11.5 tons (12.1 tonnes)
Crew five
Armament one 105-mm le FH 18/2 (L/28) field howitzer with 32 rounds and one 7.92-mm MG 34 machine-gun with 600 rounds
Armour hull nose and driver's plate, glacis 10 mm, sides 15 mm, decking 10 mm, belly 5 mm, rear 8–15 mm; superstructure front 12 mm, sides 10 mm, rear 8 mm
Range 90 miles
Height 7 feet 8 inches (2.32 m)
Other details as PzKpfw II Ausf F tank

rear superstructure. Some 682 were converted during 1943 and 1944, mostly by Famo in Warsaw and they saw wide service in the self-propelled artillery battalions of the *Panzer* and *Panzer Grenadier* divisions.

The *PzKpfw* II *Ausf* D and E were special (35-mph or 56-km/h) versions built in 1938–9 by Daimler Benz as *Schnellkampfwagen* (fast fighting vehicles) for the light divisions. These 250 vehicles had torsion-bar suspension and large wheels of the Christie type. Apparently few reached the formations for which they were intended and went instead to *Panzer* Regiment Eight – part of independent *Panzer* Brigade

Four until the latter's formation into Tenth *Panzer* Division in 1939. The new suspension had a disappointing cross-country performance and, in 1940, 95 were converted to *Flammpanzer* II flamethrower vehicles (sometimes called Flamingo) with two forward-mounted flame-guns and a small machine-gun turret. This chassis was also later used as a mount for the Soviet 76·2-mm gun in an open shield, on top of a high box-like superstructure. Both the unmodified weapon designated *FK* 296 (*r*) and the *PaK* 36(*r*), modified with a muzzle brake to take German length cartridge cases, were used. Known as the *Panzerjäger* II *Ausf* D or E *für* 7·62 cm *PaK* 36 (*r*), this was given the ordinance number *SdKfz* 132 and was also sometimes called *Marder* II. Some later vehicles had the later *PaK* 39(*r*) weapon or the German *PaK* 40/2. Alkett converted 185 in 1942; some *Flammpanzer* chassis were used latterly as the former conversion had not been entirely successful and the need for mobile anti-tank defence was more pressing. The tank destroyers were mainly used in Russia where they provided for a time the only means of giving the German divisions proper mobile protection against Soviet armour.

A lightened *PzKpfw* II prototype, designated *VK* 901 had been built in 1939 with an interleaved wheel suspension but neither it, nor a more heavily armoured infantry support *VK* 1601, was accepted for mass production. A compromise *VK* 1300 series development (*VK* 1303) was finally accepted in 1943 as the *PzKpfw* II *Ausf* L, later *Panzerspähwagen* II *Luchs* (Lynx), a reconnaissance tank issued to the *Panzer* divisions; but few were built due to other production priorities. This was the final *PzKpfw* II derivative to see action.

Above: One of the most important German self-propelled guns of the war – the Wespe (Wasp)
Left: Although unsuccessful as tanks, the PzKpfw II Ausf D and E chassis, with their special large wheel suspensions, found a new lease of life in 1942 as chassis for the captured Russian PaK 36(r). They were the forerunners of the large number of Marder II tank destroyers which utilized the more conventional PzKpfw II chassis

PzKpfw III

In 1935, after experience gained with the design of smaller tanks had been consolidated, a specification was issued for the larger 15-ton 'light tank' which Guderian intended to be the major weapon of his armoured divisions. It was to have a high-velocity gun and have a five man crew – gunner, loader, driver, wireless operator and commander – to enable each member to concentrate on his own tasks. For maximum liaison, communications between driver, wireless operator and commander were connected to the external radio. There was considerable debate over the armament of the new vehicle. The Mechanized Troops Inspectorate wanted a 50-mm weapon but the Ordnance Department felt that the standard infantry 37-mm anti-tank gun would be sufficient. The latter view eventually prevailed and the smaller weapon was chosen but it was also decided that the turret ring would be made large enough for up-gunning should it become necessary.

In 1936 the first prototypes appeared designated *Zugführerwagen* (ZW – platoon commander's vehicle) from MAN, Krupp, Rheinmetall Borsig and Daimler Benz. The last-named version was chosen and the first ten production vehicles, designated 1/*ZW Ausf* A, built. The initial suspension consisted of five, large, coil-sprung road wheels each side, but the development of the tank was seriously delayed by a long search to find a better design. It was only just before the outbreak of war, after three years' time-consuming development that the definitive suspension was fitted to the *Ausf* E using torsion bars connected to six medium-sized road wheels each side. A completely new, advanced Maybach pre-selector transmission was also fitted with ten forward speeds and one

reverse; gear change and steering were both power-assisted. The design of the front plate was improved with new driver's visor and machine-gun mounting, but armour thickness (30 mm) and the engine, a 120 TR of 320 hp, were the same as the *Ausf* D. Some 41 *Ausf* E were built and after successful trials this design was standardized as the *PzKpfw* III (3·7 cm) (*SdKfz* 141); in September 1939, 98 of the above *Ausf* D and E pre-production tanks were available for service with the *Panzer Lehr* (Demonstration) Battalion and a few examples with the Panzer Divisions for the invasion of Poland.

To speed up production, manufacture of the *PzKpfw* III was spread out among several firms – Alkett, Wegmann, Daimler Benz, Henschel, Famo, MAN and MNH – and the hull of the *PzKpfw* III was divided into four prefabricated welded assemblies – hull, front superstructure, rear superstructure and turret. But output was slow as the concerns chosen for the programme were unused to the mass-production of motor vehicles and others such as Ford and Opel were not considered due to the fact that they were not nationally owned. The first major production

PzKpfw III Ausf E
Armament one 45-calibre 37-mm anti-tank gun with 120 rounds and three 7.92-mm MG 34 machine-guns with 3,750 rounds.
Other details as PzKpfw III Ausf F

Above: A PzKpfw III Ausf E as used in the conquest of France in 1940. Note the 45-calibre 37-mm gun with internal mantlet and lack of turret stowage bin. The camouflage is based on the standard contemporary dark 'Panzer Grey' with green patches added for combat service. With this model and earlier types two 7.92-mm MG 34 machine-guns were usually mounted co-axially with the main armament; 120 rounds of 37-mm ammunition were carried. Only 41 of this type were built and they constituted the last of a long line of pre-production variants. The Ausf E introduced the standard PzKpfw III torsion bar suspension. PzKpfw III Ausf E tanks were later fitted with 50-mm guns
Below: A PzKpfw III Ausf J loaded down with extra stowage bins finds its wider tracks useful in the final unsuccessful push for Moscow in December 1941. A national flag is draped over the turret for identification

PzKpfw III Ausf F
Weight 20 tons (20.3 tonnes)
Crew five
Armament one 50-mm KwK L/42 gun with 99
rounds and two 7.92-mm MG 34 machine-guns
with 3,750 rounds
Armour hull nose 30 mm, glacis 25 mm, driver's
plate 30 mm, sides 30 mm, decking 17 mm, belly
16 mm, tail 21 mm; turret front, sides and rear
30 mm, top 10 mm
Engine one Maybach HL 120 TRM V-12 water-
cooled petrol, 300-hp
Speed 25 mph (40 km/h)
Range 109 miles (175 km)
Trench crossing 7 feet 7 inches (2.3 m)
Vertical step 2 feet (60 cm)
Fording 2 feet 7 inches (80 cm)
Overall length 17 feet 9 inches (5.41 m)
Width 9 feet 7 inches (2.92 m)
Height 8 feet 3 inches (2.51 m)

Above: *The Ausf F was the first major production
variant of the PzKpfw III. Note the 42-calibre
50-mm gun in an external mantlet, turret venti-
lator and stowage box. Early Ausf Fs had similar
guns and mantlets to the Ausf E illustrated previously. This particular tank is one of those sent
to Africa to form Deutsche Afrika Korps: note the
palm tree and swastika marking on the left hull
front. Next to it is the divisional sign of the 15th
Panzer Division, sent to reinforce Rommel*

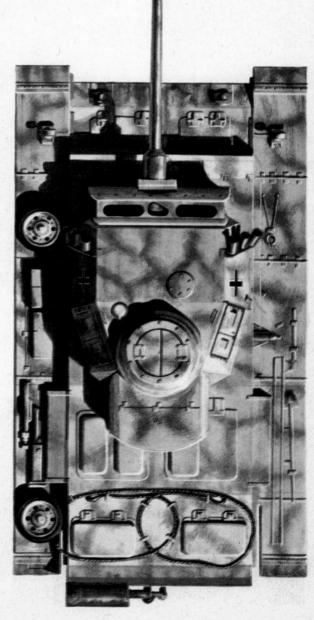

PzKpfw III Ausf M
Weight 20.8 tons (21.13 tonnes)
Armament one 60-calibre KwK 39 gun with
98 rounds and two 7.92-mm MG 34 machine-guns
with 2,550 rounds
Armour hull nose 50 mm, driver's plate 50 mm
and 20 mm, tail 50 mm; turret front 57 and
20 mm, sides and rear 30 mm
Range 93 miles (155 km)
Overall length 21 feet 6 inches (6.55 m)
Width 9 feet 9 inches (2.97 m)
Other details as PzKpfw Ausf F

Right: *A PzKpfw III Ausf M showing the several*
differences between this late vehicle and the earlier
Ausf F opposite. Note extra spaced armour added
to the mantlet and re-designed thicker driver's
plate, new 60-calibre KwK 39 gun, improved
cupola, absence of side escape hatches, new driving
sprockets and idlers, re-arranged return rollers
and wider tracks. The re-designed engine access
hatches and new exhaust system were introduced
on the Ausf M to allow wading up to 5 feet (1.52 m)

mark was the *Ausf F*, little changed from the E except for improved turret ventilation and a slightly derated 300-hp TRM engine.

By the end of 1939, 157 *PzKpfw* IIIs of all types had been built and by May 1940 there were 349 available to take part in the French invasion. Another 39 converted to armoured command vehicles enabled higher commanders of *Panzer* formations to stay up with their leading troops, a vital aid in blitzkrieg operations. On 10 May, 1940 the majority of *PzKpfw* IIIs were concentrated in Guderian's XIX *Panzer* Corps, whose task it was to make the decisive break-through in the Ardennes. Here their success was due more to the *PzKpfw* IIIs good crew layout, which assisted well co-ordinated mobile operations, than to its rather poor armament and protection. The L/45 37-mm gun with a muzzle velocity of 2,500 fps (762 m/s) could not penetrate any but the least protected enemy tanks and 30-mm armour was little protection from most Allied guns. The shortcomings of this gun had become apparent long before and in 1939 orders had been given to Krupp to develop a new 50-mm tank gun for the *PzKpfw* III. Forty *Ausf Fs*, with the new 50-mm *KwK* L/42, were rushed into action before the end of the French campaign but had little affect on the outcome.

After the lessons of France, Hitler ordered the up-gunning of the *PzKpfw* III with the longer *L/60* 50-mm anti-tank gun; but to save time the Army continued fitting the *L/42*. *Ausf Es* and Fs were retro-fitted with this gun which was in a new external mantlet. New Fs and, from October, *Ausf Gs* with slightly modified cupolas and driver's visors, were fitted as new – although the first Gs had 37-mm guns as the 50-mm remained in short supply. Some Gs were fitted with air filters and improved ventilation as *Ausf G (Tp)* (Tropical) and these served in the Western Desert. In this theatre, although the *PzKpfw* III was vulnerable to the British two-pounder (40-mm) gun (at least until later increases in protection) its armament proved effective against all British tanks except the Matilda. Although the 50-mm gun's AP performance was less good

in actual penetration, its projectile carried a high explosive charge, inflicting more permanent damage on enemy armour than that of the British two-pounder's (40-mm) solid shot. High explosive shells were also carried, useful for action against anti-tank guns; it was a particular weakness of British tanks that their two-pounder (40-mm) guns did not have this facility.

At the end of 1940 yet another new version appeared, the *Ausf H* which embodied the results of combat experience in improved armour protection. Extra 30-mm plates were bolted and welded to the hull front; wider tracks of 400 as against 360 mm were introduced to compensate for the extra weight and there was a new manual gear-box with only six forward speeds as the older one had been unnecessarily complex. Older models were retro-fitted to the new standards. There was also a command

version (*Panzerbefehlswagen* II *Ausf* C, later H) with a dummy gun. Used in North Africa from 1941 the up-armoured *PzKpfw* IIIs (both *Ausf* H and *Ausf* G modified in the field) proved unexpectedly difficult to defeat with the two-pounder (40-mm) gun, previously effective against the 30-mm plates.

When the Germans invaded Russia 1,440 *PzKpfw* IIIs were available for service. Initially, 965 were used and they were the backbone of the strongest *Panzer* divisions' tank regiments, equipping two out of the three companies of each of their tank battalions. In addition to the standard vehicles there were others fitted for deep wading which were used in the initial offensive across the River Bug and later across the Dnieper. The *PzKpfw* III was adequate for dealing with the older Soviet tanks but the KV and T-34 tanks with their thick well-shaped

Above: *All types of PzKpfw III from Ausf F onwards fought in North Africa. The protection of this early Ausf J with short 50-mm gun has been modified to Ausf L standard with extra 20-mm spaced armour on the driver's plate and mantlet. The tank was knocked out during the battles around Alamein in 1942*
Below: *One of the 75-mm armed PzKpfw III Ausf N gunfire support tanks attached to the 501st Heavy Tank Battalion of Tigers knocked out in Tunisia. This PzKpfw III model was sometimes known as the Sturmpanzer III and was designed to provide a suitable infantry support tank for the Panzergrenadier divisions*

armour and powerful guns proved difficult to defeat. Up-gunning could no longer be postponed and as Hitler was furious that his orders had been ignored, plans for the development of a tank version of the longer *L/60* 50-mm weapon were at last put in hand.

The new *Ausf J* (*SdKfz* 141/1) was built with heavier armour of 50 mm all round, which was stronger than the 60-mm welded appliqué armour of its predecessors. The driver's visor was again changed and a new ball-mounting

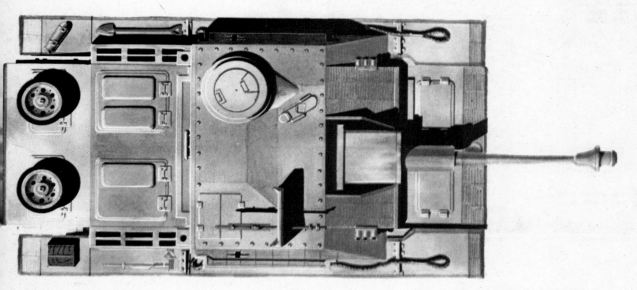

for the hull *MG* 34 adopted. Mechanical steering was fitted and other details changed to assist mass-production. From November the new L/60 50-mm gun began to be fitted and 40 *Ausf* Js were constructed by the end of the year with this weapon. The *KwK* 39 L/60 had a muzzle velocity with normal AP rounds of 2,700 fps (822 m/s), or 3,835 fps (1168 m/s) with *PzGr* 40, but even this was soon found to be insufficient. These first 'Mark III Specials' only reached the Western Desert in May 1942.

Only 862 *PzKpfw* IIIs had been built in 1940 and when the invasion of Russia boosted demand to 7,992 vehicles for 36 *Panzer* divisions (twice the total existing German armoured fighting vehicle strength) German industry, demobilized from a not very high level of war production after the fall of France, was hard pressed to meet its targets. Plans to develop a replacement 22 ton *VK* 2001 (DB) or *ZW* 40 tank were soon dropped and another factory MIAG was brought into the *PzKpfw* III programme. Still only 1,713 tanks of this type were built in 1941 and even by 1942 production targets of 190 vehicles a month were not being met. Some of these were of yet another model, the

Ausf L, also L/60 armed. To increase protection at low cost, a spaced 20-mm armour plate was added to the mantlet and hull front. A special *Ausf* L *(Trop)* was developed with improved ventilation, filters and hatches; these were widely used in North Africa from mid-1942.

Some 2,605 *PzKpfw* IIIs were built in 1942 (1,907 with the *KwK* 39) as German industry at last began to mobilize itself for total war. In order to simplify production the next *Ausf* M dispensed with the vision ports and escape hatches in the hull sides and it was also modified to wade up to five feet (1·52 m). By the end of the year the *PzKpfw* III was outmoded as a battle tank and the final variant appeared as the *Ausf* N (*SdKfz* 141/2) close support tank with low velocity L/24 75-mm guns taken from *PzKpfw* IVs. This gun had inferior AP performance to the 50-mm L/60 but it was a better weapon for HE support and the N was designed to provide the vehicles for the tank battalions of *Panzergrenadier* divisions. Some were also allocated to *Tiger* heavy tank battalions. The first *Ausf* L were modified to N standard and saw action by the end of 1942; 660 were converted or built new up to August 1943.

Sturmgeschutz III Ausf G
Weight 23.5 tons (23.9 tonnes)
Crew four
Armament one 75-mm Stuk 40 (L/48) gun with 54 rounds and one 7.92-mm MG 34 machine-gun with 600 rounds
Armour nose 80 mm, driver's plate 50 and 30 mm, sides 30 mm, decking 11–17 mm, belly 16 mm, tail 30 mm
Range 105 miles (169 km)
Overall length 22 feet 2½ inches (6.77 m)
Width 9 feet 8½ inches (2.96 m)
Height 7 feet 1¼ inches (2.15 m)
Other details as PzKpfw III Ausf F

Above: *These Sturmgeschutz III Ausf G, assault guns, were widely produced from late 1942. Originally under the control of the artillery arm, they were first organized into 18-gun assault gun battalions each of 3 batteries of 6 vehicles. These were later enlarged into army assault artillery brigades of up to 45 assault guns (3 batteries of 14 with 3 HQ vehicles) and a small infantry component. Assault guns were the élite troops of the artillery with an impressive record against enemy armour – 20,000 enemy tanks claimed by early 1944 alone*

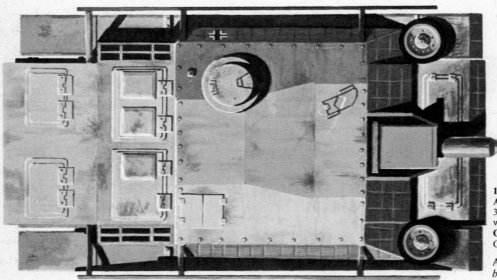

10.5-cm Sturmhaubitze 42 Ausf G
Armament one L/28 105-mm howitzer with
36 rounds and one 7.92-mm MG 34 machine-gun
with 600 rounds
Overall length 20 feet 1½ inches (6.13 m)
Other details as StuG III Ausf G

Above: *The 10.5-cm Sturmhaubitze 42 Ausf G is
basically the same as the StuG except for the
L/28 105-mm howitzer. This model has Schürtzen
protective plates fitted as was commonly done on
StuG vehicles and late model PzKpfw III tanks.
Early StuH 42s had muzzle brakes and later
StuG and StuH were fitted with better-shaped
rounded mantlets. Muzzle brakes of a new design
were adopted with some of these later StuH 42.
A 1944 type army assault artillery brigade would
contain one platoon of StuH 42 in each of its
three batteries, a total of 12 assault howitzers
per brigade. These, together with the 33 75-mm
armed StuG III, gave a powerful high velocity
armour piercing/low velocity high explosion mix
of capabilities to the unit*
Left: *A typical StuG III Ausf G fully fitted out
with protective Schürtzen abandoned to the
enemy. Note the extra armour fitted to the nose
and superstructure front*

Construction of *PzKpfw* III tanks ceased in order that production resources could be concentrated on the production of *Sturmgeschütze* (assault guns). These originated with infantry demands for an armoured close-support artillery vehicle, very necessary if all tanks were to be concentrated in the *Panzer* divisions. Daimler Benz developed a vehicle based on the *PzKpfw* III chassis with a low 50-mm armoured superstructure in which was mounted a limited traverse 75-mm L/24 tank gun. Thirty were ordered for troop trials and some took part in the invasion of France in May and June 1940 helping to clear the roads through the Ardennes. These operational tests were successful and the vehicle was ordered into production as the *Gepanzerte Selstfahrlafette für Sturmgeschutz 7·5-cm Kanone* (*SdKfz* 142), normally shortened to *StuG* III. The *Ausf* A version was mounted on an *Ausf* F (5/*ZW*) tank chassis with no side escape hatches. Alkett, the major *PzKpfw* III contractor, had built 184 by the end of 1940. With the introduction of the new *Ausf* H tank chassis the model letter changed to B, – the C and D assault gun models were basically similar. An E version was developed as a commander's vehicle with extra radio facilities. Although production was concentrated on the *PzKpfw* III tank, 548 of these assault guns were produced in 1941.

In September, Hitler, to whom the concept appealed for its economy of resources, demanded that *StuG* vehicles should be up-armoured and up-gunned. As an interim measure some were fitted with a 33-calibre 75-mm gun but by February 1942 a version of the L/43 75-mm gun

of the contemporary *PzKpfw* IV had been fitted to the *Führer* as the 7·5-cm *Sturmgeschutz* 40 *Ausf* F (*SdKfz* 142/1). After 119 vehicles the weapon was changed to the L/48 gun and this changed the designation to *Ausf* F/8. At the end of 1942, again in accordance with Hitler's wishes, 80-mm armour was fitted by means of bolting on an extra 30-mm plate over the existing 50-mm base. This produced the *Ausf* G which also had a commander's cupola and, often, a shield-mounted machine-gun. Production of these continued until the end of the war. These assault guns were in reality turretless tanks and increasing numbers were produced by Alkett, MIAG and Krupp as Germany's need for large numbers of mobile, armoured high-velocity guns outstripped her tank building capabilities. In 1942, 791 *StuG* IIIs of all types were constructed, no less than 3,041 *Ausf* Gs in 1943 and 4,850 in 1944 – 123 were produced in 1945.

With such a large amount of German resources going into assault guns and given the German tendency for competing authorities it was natural that a struggle should break out over their control between the artillery to whom they were first allocated and Guderian who wished to utilize the *StuG* IIIs to spin out his limited armoured strength and provide better anti-tank protection for the infantry divisions. The artillery strongly resisted the Inspector General of Armoured Troops' claim and it was not until the end of 1943 that assault gun units came under full armoured control.

In addition to the 75-mm gun *StuG* there was

a version mounting a 105-mm howitzer with greater HE power though at the expense of armour penetration capability. These first used the *Ausf* F superstructure but the production vehicles were 10·5-cm *Sturmhaubitze* 42 *Ausf* G (*SdKfz* 142/2). Nine 105-mm *StuH* IIIs were constructed in 1942 (including prototype), 204 in 1943 and 904 in 1944. Another assault variant mounted the 150-mm sIG 33 infantry gun. In all 15,350 *PzKpfw* III chassis were built.

PzKpfw IIIs were supplied to Hungary and friendly neutrals such as Spain and Turkey also received them. Captured examples were used by the Free Polish forces for training in the Middle East while the Soviets converted others into assault guns with 76·2-mm guns (with or without muzzle brake) in a slightly higher superstructure than the *StuG* III. As the *SU 76I* this served against its former owners and some were recaptured by the Germans and used 'third hand'! The *PzKpfw* III survived the war in the armies of Eastern Europe.

The *StuG* III was also supplied to allies, Finland, Rumania and Bulgaria receiving examples from the Germans and some were even acquired by Syria after the war.

Below: *When captured by Soviet forces PzKpfw III and Sturmgeschütze were often pressed into service against their former owners. Some PzKpfw III tanks were re-armed with 76.2-mm guns and others were converted by the Russians into assault guns. This Ausf J, however, appears to be in its original condition, as are the StuG IIIs supporting it in the usual Soviet style*

PzKpfw IV

The *PzKpfw* IV was the only German battle tank to remain in production throughout the war years and it became the major such vehicle of the German army. This, however, had never been intended. Originally the IV was seen as an artillery support vehicle only to the lighter tanks in the *Panzer* Division, equipping one company in a battalion. Hence a low-velocity, relatively high-calibre gun was fitted in order to obtain a good high-explosive capability.

The first prototype appeared in 1934 from Rheinmetall-Borsig under the pseudonym *Bataillonsführerwagen* (battalion commander's vehicle) and used a version of that firm's standard tractor. Both Krupp and MAN also produced prototypes with advanced interleaved wheel suspensions but, in order to get the tank into production quickly, the various features were combined together with the leaf-spring coupled bogie suspension of the Krupp design for the *Zugführerwagen* specification, and the result was produced by the latter manufacturer as the *I/BW Ausf* A.

The specification had called for a tank of no more than 24 tons due to the limitations of the standard German bridge although the first vehicles only weighed just over 17 tons. The suspension, which remained standard for the whole series, was composed of four pairs of wheels and there were four return rollers; a standard 250-hp Maybach HL 108R petrol engine was fitted, driving through the front sprockets and producing a speed of 18·2 mph (30 km/h); and the five-man crew were dispersed in the same efficient way as in the *PzKpfw* III, with similar communication equipment. The L/24 75-mm gun was mounted in the turret with a co-axial MG 34 machine-gun; a second machine-gun was in the hull front, set back a little from the driver's position. The turret had electrical traverse. Again, as in the early III, hull armour was thin, a mere 14·5 mm on the hull and 20 mm on the turret. Production and troop trials were dilatory and only 35 were constructed during 1936. In the following year 42 *Ausf* Bs were manufactured and 140 *Ausf* Cs in 1938. These introduced new HL 120 engines and 30-mm armour on hull (B) and turret (C) fronts. Together they were sufficient to produce a medium allocation to the tank battalions of existing *Panzer* divisions and production decreased to 45 in 1939; the majority of these were *Ausf* D with 20-mm side and rear armour.

Combat experience showed that although the type was basically sound and could finally be officially adopted for service as the *PzKpfw* IV (7·5-cm) (*SdKfz* 161) it needed further up-armouring if it was to act as a real back-up to the *PzKpfw* III. Hence the next model, the *Ausf* E, production of which began in December, had a thicker nose and appliqué plates added to the front and sides to bring protection up to 50–60 mm; older models were retro-fitted. On the *Ausf* E a new type of visor and cupola was adopted and the latter was moved forward in the turret. In February production of the definitive version began, the *Ausf* F. This reverted to a single, and therefore stronger, 50-mm front plate; a new ball machine-gun mount was fitted and the driver's visor was altered again; weight was up to over 22 tons and wider tracks were fitted (400 mm instead of 380 mm) which necessitated a widened front sprocket.

Below: *A PzKpfw IV Ausf E knocked out and captured in December 1941 near Sidi Rezegh. Note the extra armour on the superstructure front (30 mm) and the sides (20 mm) and the new lower cupola. The Afrika Korps badge is on a patch of Panzer Grey left when the tank was roughly camouflaged in desert yellow*

PzKpfw IV Ausf D
Weight 19.7 tons (20 tonnes)
Crew five
Armament one 75-mm KwK L/24 gun with 80 rounds and two 7.92-mm MG 34 machine-guns with 2,800 rounds
Armour basic: hull nose 30 mm, glacis 20 mm, driver's plate 30 mm, sides 20 mm, decking 11 mm, belly 10–20 mm, tail 20 mm; turret front 30 mm, sides and rear 20 mm, top 10 mm
Engine one Maybach HL 120 TRM V-12 water-cooled petrol, 300-hp
Speed 26 mph (42 km/h)
Range 125 miles (200 km)
Trench crossing 7 feet 7 inches (2.3 m)
Vertical step 2 feet (60 cm)
Fording 2 feet 7½ inches (80 cm)
Overall length 19 feet 4½ inches (5.91 m)
Width 9 feet 7 inches (2.92 m)
Height 8 feet 6 inches (2.59 m)

Above: *By 1943–4 most PzKpfw IVs in action were fully equipped with long 75-mm guns and Schürtzen plates, 8 mm around the turret and 5 mm on the sides. These new Ausf H vehicles (note the single cupola hatch) advancing through the outskirts of a Russian town have only the extra turret protection*
Right: *The PzKpfw IV Ausf D was introduced in 1939. Its external mantlet for the 75-mm gun and re-adoption of 7.92-mm hull machine-gun distinguished it externally from the preceding Ausf C. The side armour was also increased over the older model. Tanks of this type were progressively up-armoured and fitted with new long 75-mm guns to bring them up to the latest standards. After this model, a new type of cupola was adopted. This tank is in the condition in which it might have fought in the French campaign of 1940, or in the opening year of the campaign in Russia. The fitting under the gun is a deflector to protect the tank's aerials from the blast of the short weapon*

Altogether 278 *PzKpfw* IVs of various models were available with the medium companies of the ten *Panzer* divisions that attacked France in 1940. They provided some useful support being just able to defeat the armour of most Allied tanks. The later models were hard to penetrate at long range, and, despite their small numbers, their presence was often decisive.

Limited production continued at Krupp in 1941 and by the time Germany attacked Russia about 580 *PzKpfw* IVs were available. Demand was stepped up with the proposed expansion to 36 Armoured Divisions in July but by April 1942 the number of *PzKpfw* IVs in service had barely risen above the numbers available the year before; more factories were brought into the programme and numbers finally increased from 480 in 1941 to 964 in 1942. But this was still hardly enough as it was becoming apparent that the *PzKpfw* IV was the only German tank capable of up-gunning to penetrate the well-shaped armour of the *T-34s* and KV-1s. A long 75-mm gun, the *KsK* 40 L/43 tank gun was produced and fitted from March 1942 to the new *Ausf* F2 version of the *PzKpfw* IV – the earlier *Ausf* F now became F1. With a muzzle velocity with ordinary shot of 2,428 fps (740 m/s), and a penetration against 30-degree armour of 89 mm, this gun allowed *Panzer* units to face up to the Soviet tanks on equal terms.

A further model, the *Ausf* G, appeared in 1942 with slightly improved protection and an improved double-baffle muzzle brake on the gun. Older IVs were brought up to the latest standard as they returned to Germany for overhaul. In March 1943, in accordance with Hitler's orders of the previous year, the *Ausf* H, with 80-mm armour and an L/48 75-mm gun (2,461 fps) was introduced. To increase protection from infantry thin, 5-mm *Schürzen* (side plates)

were fitted and with Guderian's encouragement production increased: 3,073 *PzKpfw* IVs were built in 1943 and 3,161 more in 1944 to 1945. From March 1944 these were the last model, the *Ausf* J, with the electrical turret traverse replaced by a purely manual arrangement. As well as simplyifying production this also allowed an extra fuel tank to be fitted, boosting the range to 200 miles (322 km). Wire mesh *Schürtzen* were fitted to lower weight and material demands, and a new idler was also fitted. *Ostkette* wide tracks also began to be adopted from the late summer of 1944 to improve mobility.

Below: *'Guderian's Duck'. This side view of an early L/48-armed Jagdpanzer IV illustrates well both the vehicle's low silhouette and the differences between the standard vehicle and the interim model based on the normal tank chassis illustrated in the drawing on the opposite page*
Bottom: *Something of a rarity, this Bergepanzer IV recovery vehicle was knocked out in North Africa. Indeed, this may well have been the only PzKpfw IV chassis, an Ausf D, so modified. An extra weapon, possibly a flame-thrower, appears to have been added in the driver's visor, giving this specialized vehicle a useful combat capability*

PzKpfw IV/70 Zwischenlösung (Interim)
Weight 27.6 tons (28 tonnes)
Crew four or five
Armament one 75-mm StuK 42 (L/70) with 60 rounds
Armour hull nose and driver's plate 85 mm, glacis 20 mm, sides 30 mm, decking and belly 10 mm, tail 20 mm, superstructure front 80 mm, mantlet 120 mm, sides 40 mm, roof 20 mm, rear 30 mm
Speed 24 mph (38 km/h)
Range 200 miles
Trench crossing 7 feet 3 inches (2.2 m)
Fording 3 feet 3 inches (1.00 m)
Overall length 27 feet 8 inches (8.44 m)
Width 9 feet 7 inches (2.93 m)
Height 7 feet 8½ inches (2.34 m)
Other details as PzKpfw IV Ausf D tank

Above: *This special (interim) version of the PzKpfw IV/70 (Jagdpanzer IV) was designed to overcome production difficulties by utilizing the standard PzKpfw IV Ausf J chassis with new superstructure based on that of the normal Jagdpanzer. Both Alkett and Vomag built prototypes and the former was chosen for production*

In June 1944 Hitler ordered that production of the *PzKpfw* IV should be abandoned to concentrate on its tank destroyer derivative, the *Jagdpanzer* IV, which had the 3,068 fps (935 m/s) L/70 gun of the *Panther* in a limited-traverse mounting. This vehicle dated from 1942 when a request had gone out for a new heavy assault gun with 100-mm armour. Guderian was against the project from the start; he was satisfied with the development capability of the *StuG* III and was loath to diversify production of the *PzKpfw* IV which he regarded as the mainstay of the armoured forces. Development of what was to be nicknamed 'Guderian's Duck' was slow and an interim assault gun on the IV chassis with a standard *StuG* III superstructure and an L/48 75-mm gun was designed. On some of these *Sturmgeschutz* IV assault guns (*SdKfz* 163) concrete armour was added, particularly over the driver's compartment where it could be up to 100 mm thick. About 1,000 were built in 1944, on *Ausf* H and *Ausf* G chassis, and issued to both tank battalions and artillery assault gun battalions.

The *Jagdpanzer* IV had meanwhile been developed with the same L/48 gun as it took time to develop a suitable L/70 weapon. Frontal protection was 60 mm with 30-mm armour fitted at the sides. Early vehicles carried a muzzle brake on the gun but as it was mounted so low – only four feet seven inches (1·40 m) above the ground – this led to a great deal of dust from the deflected blast and later vehicles had this deleted. The L/70 was eventually adapted and armour thickness was also increased to 80 mm (front) and 40 mm (sides).

Small numbers of *PzKpfw* IV/70, as the upgunned *Jagdpanzer* IV was redesignated, were in action by August 1944. Its armament made it a formidable defensive weapon, particularly in the west against less well-protected British and American armour. However, despite ambitious production schedules only 1,531 *Jagdpanzer* IVs of all types were constructed. They usually served with the tank destroyer battalions of *Panzer* divisions.

Later examples were built with a slightly modified chassis incorporating features from the *PzKpfw* III tank, notably three return rollers instead of four. This reflected a final abortive attempt to rationalize the production of the two basic German tracked AFV chassis and

develop a common III/IV chassis on which various vehicles could be mounted. For example, Alkett designed a *Geschützwagen* (gun carriage) III/IV on a front-engined *PzKpfw* IV chassis with the sprockets and final drive of the III. There were four return rollers and the gun was carried in a lightly armoured superstructure at the rear. The most numerous vehicle on this chassis was the *Hummel* (Bumblebee) (*SdKfz* 165) which mounted a 150-mm FH 18/1 heavy field howitzer. The prototype vehicle had a muzzle brake and was mounted on a standard *PzKpfw* IV chassis but production vehicles had a clean barrel and the III/IV modifications. From 1942, 666 were built and they equipped the heavy batteries of the artillery battalions of favoured *Panzer* divisions.

From 1943 another version of the III/IV gun carriage appeared, mounting the 71-calibre 88-mm *PaK* 43/1 anti-tank gun. This heavy new weapon needed a self-propelled platform in the difficult conditions of the Eastern Front; the *Nashorn* (Rhinoceros) gave heavy tank destroyer brigades a new mobility, although for a direct fire weapon armour protection was poor. Some 150 chassis were completed as gunless ammunition carriers for both the anti-tank gun and also the howitzer variants.

Due to a mixture of conservatism and the tactical disadvantages of existing vehicles, with their high prominent superstructures and limited-traverse mounts, the artillery arm was not very happy with the concept of the self-propelled gun. Development, therefore, began on a series of *Waffenträger* (weapon carrier) vehicles which allowed the gun to be dismounted if necessary and also provided the lighter weapons with all round traverse. Two models mounting the 105-mm Le FH were produced, the *Heuschrecke* (Grasshopper) built on a slightly lengthened version of the *PzKpfw* IV chassis and a less specialized version using the III/IV gun carriage. Both proved difficult to operate and were never put into production.

The need for a heavy assault howitzer had become apparent during the severe street fighting in Russia in 1941–2 where existing tanks and armoured assault guns had insufficient high-explosive capability to deal with well-protected buildings and fortifications, and existing heavy howitzers were too lightly protected. Hitler felt the problem could be solved by a much more

Panzerjäger III/IV Nashorn (Rhinoceros)
Weight 23.6 tons (24 tonnes)
Crew four
Armament one 88-mm PaK 43/1 (L/71) gun with 40 rounds
Armour hull nose and driver's plate 30 mm, glacis 10 mm, sides 20 mm, decking and belly 15 mm, tail 22 mm, superstructure 10 mm
Fording 3 feet 3 inches (1 m)
Overall length 27 feet 8½ inches (8.44 m)
Width 9 feet 8 inches (2.95 m)
Height 9 feet 7½ inches (2.94 m)
Other details as Ausf D tank

Above: *A total of 473 of these heavy tank destroyers were constructed on the Geschützwagen III/IV, a front-engined PzKpfw IV chassis with the transmission and final drive of the PzKpfw III. The vehicle's earlier name was Hornisse (Hornet) but this was changed at Hitler's insistence to the more aggressive Nashorn (Rhinoceros)*

heavily armoured mounting for the 150-mm *sIG* 33 heavy infantry gun which would have to go on the *PzKpfw* IV chassis. The vehicles were ordered in October 1942 and in service by April of the next year as *Sturmpanzer* IV *Brummbär* (Grizzly Bear) *Sdkfz* 166. Early Grizzly Bears were on the *Ausf* F and *Ausf* G chassis with a relatively high armoured superstructure with 100-mm sloping plates at the front and 70-mm protection at the sides, with a new version of the infantry gun the *SturmHaubitze* 43 L/12 in a ball mounting in the frontal plate. Later models on the H and J chassis had several differences, notably a modified gun-mounting with longer 'collar', a new driver's compartment with periscopes and in the last production run a new roomier superstructure with a machine-gun, lack of which had proved a serious weakness. A total of 313 Grizzly Bears saw service with the infantry gun companies of *Panzergrenadier* regiments and artillery units in Russia, Italy and France. They were powerful, if specialized, vehicles in the infantry support role but reliability could be erratic due to the chassis being overloaded.

As the war progressed so the Germans began to lose air superiority and their armoured units became very vulnerable to Allied air attack. Suitable protection was urgently required and from 1943 *PzKpfw* IV chassis were diverted to become *Flakpanzer* IV anti-aircraft vehicles. Hitler demanded a *Flakpanzer* with twin 37-mm guns but as an interim measure either a single

Sturmpanzer IV Brummbär (Grizzly Bear)
Weight 27.7 tons (28.2 tonnes)
Crew five
Armament one 150-mm StuH 53 (L/12) howitzer
with 38 rounds
Armour hull nose 80 mm, sides 30 mm, decking
and tail 20 mm, belly 10 mm; superstructure
front 100 mm, sides 30–70 mm, top 20 mm,
rear 20–60 mm
Speed 24 mph (38 km/h)
Trench crossing 7 feet 3 inches (2.2 m)
Fording 3 feet 1½ inches (95 cm)
Height 8 feet (2.44 m)
Other details as Ausf D tank

*Right: A middle production Brummbär built in
1944 after the success of the first 60 built in late
Spring 1943. Note the long 'sleeve' on the howitzer
barrel and the heavily armoured driver's position
with periscopes, instead of direct vision as on the
earlier model. PzKpfw IV type Schürtzen were
usually carried by these vehicles. The last Brummbär produced had a new superstructure with more
vertical sides. Sturmpanzer battalions could de-
ploy up to 45 of these powerful assault howitzers*

37-mm *FlaK* 43 or the quadruple 20-mm *Flakvierling* 38 was mounted in a high open 10-mm protected superstructure, the sides of which could drop to give all round traverse – if little protection to the gun crew who were behind a small open shield. However, they did provide some degree of extra mobility for the anti-aircraft platoons of tank regiments and 211 of these high, box-shaped *'Mobelwagen'* (furniture vans) were converted from *Ausf* H and J chassis.

A much better vehicle appeared in December 1943 which put the *Flakvierling* weapon in a 16-mm armoured revolving turret. This was known as *Wirbelwind* (Whirlwind) and was built by Ostbau using an *Ausf J* chassis. It was supplemented from March 1944 by the *Ostwind* (East Wind), built by Deutsche Eisenwerke, which put the 37-mm *FlaK* 43 in a slightly better protected 25-mm turret. The rates of fire of these weapons were respectively 800 to 1,800 rounds per minute and 80 to 160 rounds. Some 140 *Wirbelwind* and 40 *Ostwind* vehicles were built and some saw service but they could not do a great deal to mitigate the effects of Allied air power. However, even these vehicles were only considered as interim designs due to their open-topped turrets. A more permanent *leichte Flakpanzer* IV *Kugelblitz* (Fireball) was developed and built by Deutsche Eisenwerke with twin 30-mm *FlaK* 103/38 guns, developed from aircraft cannon, mounted in a fully rotating turret – together these could deliver up to 900 rounds per minute. Only five or six vehicles were completed and on troop trials when the war ended.

Over 10,500 vehicles were produced on the *PzKpfw* IV chassis and its derivatives including over 7,000 tanks. Except on the Eastern Front during 1941 and 1942, before up-gunning, the IV could usually perform adequately on the battlefield; although in the terms of 1944 and 1945 it was hardly up to the highest contemporary standards in protection or gun-power. Its capacity for constant improvement, however, bore witness to the foresight of its original designers. The IV enabled the Germans to keep a satisfactory vehicle coming off the production lines while developments of better tanks were completed, and Guderian was right to insist on its continued production. The 'Mark IV' was less famous than its later named compatriots but it was never replaced by the *Panther* and fought right up to the end of the war.

Flakpanzer IV Wirbelwind (Whirlwind)
Armament four 20-mm Flakvierling 38s with 3,200 rounds, one hull machine-gun with 1,350 rounds
Armour hull nose and driver's plate 80 mm, sides 16 mm
Other details as the PzKpfw Ausf D

Left: *A total of three or four of these quadruple 20-mm anti-aircraft vehicles the Flakpanzer IV Wirbelwind (Whirlwind) were deployed with the HQ companies of individual Panzer battalions from 1944. In all 3,200 rounds of 20-mm ammunition were carried, enough for 40 minutes at minimum firing rate; 1,350 rounds were carried for the hull machine-gun. Problems were faced with the relatively slow speed of traverse of the turret which was armoured to 16 mm. Hull armour was as in the Ausf J with 80 mm on the nose and driver's plate and 30 mm on the sides*

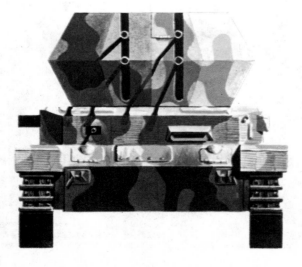

PzKpfw 35(t) and 38(t)

service in 1936 as the *LT 35* and it went into production at both plants; the ČKD vehicles had small differences from those of Škoda.

Some 298 *LT* 35s were in service with the Czechs by 1938, in which year they were used against the Sudeten Nazi *Freikorps* units during the period of tension leading up to the Munich Agreement. In 1939 some passed to Slovakia while others were taken over by the *Wehrmacht*, who kept the *LT* 35 in production as the *PzKpfw* 35(*t*) (*t* for *tschechisch* – Czech). Some were used during the invasion of Poland and 106 were on hand with the Third and Sixth *Panzer* Divisions when France was invaded. They were adequate substitutes for *PzKpfw* IIIs, more or less similarly protected – except for the rivets – but with guns of higher velocity (2,620 fps against 2,500 – 789 m/s against 762 m/s). The crew distribution of the 35(*t*) was not quite so lavish, commander, driver, gunner and loader/radio operator, but the advanced and now reliable transmission made it easy to keep up high average speeds over long distances and exploit the robustness of the suspension.

These attributes were also useful during the invasion of Russia, by which time 190 *PzKpfw* 35(*t*) tanks were available. However, the new Soviet tanks finally made the 35(*t*) obsolete althought some chassis were converted for use as tractors and self-propelled 80-mm mortar carriages. A few were also kept by the Germans for second line policing duties.

The major Czech tank used by German forces was the ČKD/Praga *TNHP* which they redesignated *PzKpfw* 38(*t*). This model had an

When Germany finally dismembered Czechoslovakia in 1939 she inherited a long-established armaments industry that was already a noted producer of armoured fighting vehicles. The main manufacturers were Škoda and Českomoravská Kolben Daněk (ČKD) with Praga, who in 1935 had combined their research to develop a 10½-ton light tank. Based on Škoda's S II, the S IIa had a similar rear-mounted six-cylinder engine of 120-hp, driving through the rear sprockets to leave the fighting compartment uncluttered by the transmission. Both steering and gear change were pneumatically assisted to ease the strain on the driver, and an improved leaf-spring suspension was fitted with two sets of double bogie wheel pairs each side which equalized wear and gave long track life. Frontal armour protection was 35-mm to 28-mm and the gun remained the Škoda A3 with a prominent hydraulic buffer. A weakness of the design was the large-scale use of rivets in the hull construction: when hit by hostile fire these tended to fly off inside the tank with potentially disastrous results for the crew. It was accepted for Czech

Above: This picture depicts a Czech LT-35 in pre-occupation yellow, green and brown camouflage. These vehicles formed a significant part of the Panzer forces during their opening victories. Originally very unreliable due to their mechanical complexity these problems were largely solved by the time the tanks went into action

Below: A PzKpfw 38(t) Ausf B dismounts from an armoured train. Armoured train units formed the least remembered part of the Panzerwaffe

improved suspension based on four elliptically-sprung large rubber-tyred road wheels. Two light tanks were initially produced with these features, a small four ton *AH* IV with two machine-guns and single return roller and a larger eight ton *TNH* with 100 hp engine, turret mounted 20-mm gun (in the prototype) and two return rollers. The large wheels may have been designed with the Middle East terrain in mind as Iran was the first customer for both, ordering 50 of each in 1935. They were delivered by 1937, the bigger vehicles with 37-mm guns as the *TNHP* (*P* for Persia). After competitive trials the *TNHP* was chosen for the Czech army as the *LT* 38 with a 125-hp Praga petrol engine and a Škoda turret armed with a 47·8-calibre A7 37·2-mm gun.

Only about 80 of these tanks were in service by March 1939 but production continued after the German occupation as the *PzKpfw* 38(*t*). They were used to equip Seventh and Eighth *Panzer* Divisions, who fielded 228 for the invasion of France in May 1940. With 25-mm armour they were only slightly less well-protected than the *PzKpfw* IIIs and *PzKpfw* IVs but their more powerful guns made up for this, and despite the weakness of a riveted hull the 38(*t*) soon made a

name for itself as a good and reliable tank. By the end of the year, 432 were on strength and by the time of the invasion of Russia over 750. At this period, in fact, the 38(*t*) formed a good 25 per cent of Germany's entire tank force.

CKD, which became the Böhmisch Mährische Maschinenfabrik A G in 1940, produced some 1,168 *PzKpfw* 38(*t*)s before production of the tanks ceased in 1942. There were eight marks from *Ausf* A (the original 150 Czech vehicles) to G, while a number ordered by Sweden, but seized by the Germans before delivery, became *Ausf* S. There were only small differences between marks but later tanks had an extra 25-mm of armour attached to the nose and frontal plate. There were the usual command versions of all marks with extra radio equipment.

It was only the advent of the *T-34* and KV series that forced the tank's obsolescence for the chassis was too light for up-gunning with a 75-mm *L*/48 and the entire *PzKpfw* IV turret. A light reconnaissance vehicle, the *Aufklärungspanzer* 38(*t*) (*SdKfz* 140/1), on the standard chassis, did appear in limited quantities in 1943 and 70 were in action the next year. Old 38(*t*) tanks lost their turrets to be used as tractors and ammunition carriers while a few were fitted as

smoke-screen layers, in which role they were known as *PzKpfw* 38(*t*) *mit Nebel Ausrüstung*.

Reliable and easy to maintain the *TNH* chassis was too valuable to lose and for the rest of the war its production continued as a self-propelled gun carriage. With the appearance of the latest Soviet tanks great stress had been put on the need for adequate anti-tank protection for the German forces and, just as the *PzKpfw* II chassis was pressed into service as a *Panzerjäger* anti-tank gun carrier, so the *TNH* seemed to offer an immediate solution to the problem of mobile anti-tank protection.

From March 1942 production began of a simple conversion which placed the Russian 54·8-calibre Model 36 76·2-mm field gun (the only guns capable of adequately penetrating Russian armour) on the 38(*t*) chassis. Captured examples of these guns were modified to take the longer German cartridge case and fitted with muzzle brakes as the 7·62-cm *PaK* 36(*r*). The gun had a muzzle velocity of 2,430 fps (740 m/s) or 3,249 fps (990 m/s) with *PzGr* 40 and could penetrate 83 mm of 30 degree armour at 500 yards (457 m) or 118 mm with *PzGr* 40. It was mounted centrally on the turretless 38(*t*) *Ausf* G chassis in a low, armoured superstructure

Left: This PzKpfw 38(t) artwork represents a typical vehicle of the 7th and 8th Panzer divisions in May 1940. Both these units played important parts in the German victory in the west. The turret markings show this particular tank to be the first tank of the third platoon of the sixth company of its regiment. The tank is finished in the standard 'Panzer Grey'

PzKpfw 38(t) Ausf D
Weight 8.4 tons (8.5 tonnes)
Crew four
Armament one 37.2-mm Škoda A7 (L/47.8) gun with 90 rounds and two 7.92-mm MG 37(*t*) (Model 37) machine-guns with 2,550 rounds
Armour hull nose, glacis and driver's plate 25 mm, sides 15–19 mm, decking 10 mm, belly 8 mm, tail 12 mm; turret front and sides 25 mm, top 10 mm, rear 15 mm
Engine one Praga EPA Model I inline six-cylinder, liquid-cooled petrol, 125-hp
Speed 35 mph (56 km/h)
Range 125 miles (200 km)
Trench crossing 6 feet 1 inch (1.85 m)
Vertical step 2 feet 7½ inches (80 cm)
Fording 3 feet (90 cm)
Overall length 15 feet 2 inches (4.62 m)
Width 6 feet 9 inches (2.06 m)
Height 7 feet 11 inches (2.41 m)

Above: *This first version of the Marder III Panzerjäger mounting the re-chambered Soviet M-36 76.2-mm gun was a modification of the PzKpfw 38(t) Ausf G chassis, note the 'straight' up-armoured driver's plate compared with the earlier artwork. The modifications to the basic tank were kept to a minimum to speed entry into service. Although very much an expedient this first 38(t) based tank destroyer proved most useful in both North Africa and Russia. The use of a captured Russian gun on a foreign chassis illustrates well the forced resourcefulness of German weapons procurement. The camouflage is a standard green on sand pattern typical of those used in both the Marder III's combat theatres*

Marder III
Weight 10.5 tons (10.7 tonnes)
Crew four
Armament one 76.2-mm PaK 36(r) (L/54.8) gun with 30 rounds and one 7.92-mm MG 37(t) machine-gun with 1,500 rounds
Armour hull nose and driver's plate 25 + 25 mm, sides and rear 15 mm, superstructure front and sides 16 mm, gun shield 11 mm
Engine one Praga EPA Model III, 125 hp
Speed 26 mph (42 km/h)
Range 115 miles (185 km)
Overall length 21 feet 1 inch (6.43 m)
Height 8 feet 2½ inches (2.5 m)
Other details as PzKpfw IV Ausf D

with a three-sided shield around the gun itself to protect the two-man crew. The driver and radio operator remained in the hull front, the latter still working his *MG* 37(*t*) machine-gun. The full designation was *Panzerjäger* 38 *für* 7·62 cm *PaK* 36 (*SdKfz* 139), but the name soon adopted was *Marder* (Marten) III.

By May 1942 some 120 had been built and all but three of these appear to have been sent to North Africa to deal with the Matilda – the Commonwealth forces were so impressed with the performance of the re-chambered German gun that they thought they were facing mobile 88-mm weapons! The remainder of the 344 vehicles produced in 1942 went to Russia, as originally intended, where allocated to the tank destroyer units of infantry and *Panzer* divisions they provided much needed support.

In May it was decided to supplement, and eventually replace, these stop-gap vehicles with a *Panzerjäger* mounting the new German 46-calibre 75-mm *PaK* 40/3 of similar performance to the Russian weapon and from June the new *Marder* III (*SdKfz* 138) began to appear. It was somewhat different to the *SdKfz* 139 with the gun's standard shield extended round the front and sides to give better protection to the gun crew. Some 400 were built in all; during production the Praga engine was up-rated to 150 hp and the de-

signation changed to *Ausf* H. This chassis was also used to provide a mobile mount for the 150-mm *sIG* 33 heavy infantry gun in the front of a large open superstructure. Designated *SdKfz* 138/1, production began in 1943 and the vehicle soon acquired the name *Bison*. It was issued to the infantry gun companies of *Panzergrenadier* regiments to provide their basic direct-fire heavy-support weapon with mobility.

However, all these vehicles were in the nature of improvisations on what was still basically a tank chassis and considerable re-design took place at BMM to specialize the chassis for the self-propelled gun role. The engine was moved from the rear to a central position with a new sloping front plate from which the machine-gun was deleted. The new one fighting compartment moved to the rear. This much better balanced layout, was designated *Ausf* M and had only a single return roller instead of the previous two. BMM produced both *Marder* IIIs and *Bison* on the new chassis with slightly differently shaped superstructures. This brought the totals of both types to 1,217 and 360 respectively by the time production ceased in May 1944, to concentrate all BMMs production on the *Hetzer*.

This *Jagdpanzer* 38(*t*) had been developed as a specialized light assault gun for the anti-tank battalions of the infantry divisions. The

Jagdpanzer 38(t) Hetzer
Weight 15.7 tons (16 tonnes)
Crew four
Armament one 75-mm PaK 39 (L/48) gun with
41 rounds and one 7.92-mm MG 34 machine-gun
with 600 rounds
Armour front 60 mm, sides 20 mm, decking and
tail 8 mm
Engine one Prage EPA/AC Model IV, inline six
cylinder 150 hp
Speed 26 mph (42 km/h)
Range 112 miles (180 km)
Trench crossing 4 feet 3 inches (1.3 m)
Vertical step 25 inches (64 cm)
Fording 3 feet (90 cm)
Overall length 20 feet 7 inches (6.27 m)
Width 8 feet 8 inches (2.63 m)
Height 6 feet 11 inches (2.1 m)
Other details as PzKpfw 38(t) Ausf D

Above: *The Hetzer was a useful little tank
destroyer although design weaknesses made it
unpopular with its crews. The roof-mounted
machine-gun could be traversed and fired from
inside. The concept of this vehicle fitted Guderian's
idea of a Jagdpanzer to defend the infantry from
armour much better than the more impressive
larger vehicles*

reliable 38(t) chassis was widened to accept a modified version of the *PzKpfw* IVs L/48 gun, designated *PaK* 39 L/48, without muzzle brake, in the front plate of a low, heavily-sloped super-structure. The tracks were also strengthened and widened slightly to improve mobility. A re-motely controlled machine-gun was fitted to the superstructure to defend from hostile infantry. The prototype appeared in 1943 and from May the next year *Hetzer* (Baiter) began to enter service. At first only BMM produced the vehicle but from September 1944 Skoda also joined the programme. The *Saukopf* mantlet was en-larged to increase protection from bullet splash at maximum traverse and as production con-tinued simplified wheels and idlers were adopted. A total of 1,577 were built.

Although *Hetzer* was a well-designed vehicle externally, it had many drawbacks. The traverse of the gun was the least of any German *Jagd-*panzer – 11 degrees to the right and 5 degrees to the left – which meant that the whole *Hetzer* usually had to be slewed to cover a target moving across the front thus exposing the limited side armour to the enemy. The crew layout was also poor with the loader and gunner on the left-hand side of a gun designed for right-handed operation; they were also isolated from the ammunition supply. The commander was re-mote in the right-hand rear of the vehicle with inadequate means of observation – and he could hardly co-operate with the gunner and driver in order to engage targets. Nevertheless, the *Hetzer* provided a real improvement in terms of armour over the more improvised *Panzer-jäger* it replaced and it went into service in both East and West. A number used in the Ardennes offensive were built with flame-throwers as *Flammpanzer* 38(t). A flame gun replaced the *PaK* 39 with a tube mounted over it to disguise

Below: *Despite its popularity among modern modellers, the Hetzer only saw service in the last year of war. The Czechs kept the vehicle in pro-duction after 1945 and Switzerland purchased a number for service with her Army. The wavy multi-coloured camouflage scheme applied to the vehicle in the photograph was often used on Hetzer*

Flakpanzer 38(t)
Weight 9.6 tons (9.8 tonnes)
Crew five
Armament one 20-mm Flak 38 automatic AA gun
Overall length 15 feet 1 inch (4.6 m)
Width 7 feet 1 inch (2.15 m)
Height 7 feet 5 inches (2.25 m)
Other details as PzKpfw 38(t)

Right: *Another vehicle on the front-engined 38(t) Ausf M self-propelled carriage was the Flakpanzer 38(t) (2 cm) (SdKfz 140). This was an improvisation necessitated by the growing need to defend Panzer formations from allied air superiority, an established fact on all fronts by 1943–4. The 9.6 ton (9.8 tonne) five-man vehicle mounted a single 20-mm FlaK 38 automatic AA gun. Despite a practical rate of fire of 220 rounds per minute this was hardly a very heavy armament for such a large chassis. Protection for the crew in action was minimal as the lightly armoured superstructure had to swing down to give all round traverse. Some were issued to the AA platoons of tank battalions but only 162 had been built by the time production of the Ausf M chassis ceased in 1944*

Opposite page, top: *The ubiquitous PzKpfw 38(t) was also used to provide mobility for the 150-mm sIG 33 infantry gun for the support of Panzergrenadiers. The first 'Bison' was as usual something of a makeshift utilizing the basic tank chassis but nevertheless these vehicles proved very useful in the direct infantry support role and saw widespread use*

Opposite page, bottom: *The new front-engined Ausf M version of the PzKpfw 38(t) chassis provided a much better balanced Marder III as this rear view shows. Almost 800 of this later type were built compared with about half that number of the earlier rear engined 75-mm Panzerjäger 38(t)*

the fitting; 154 gallons of fuel were carried and the projector had a range of 66 yards (60·35 m). Several others were completed with a winch replacing the gun as *Bergepanzer* 38(*t*).

In 1944 a programme to adopt the basic rugged Czech chassis as a standard German type was drawn up; all factories that had been producing the *PzKpfw* IV were to be switched to the production of a new 38(*d*) (*deutsche* – German) chassis to provide a whole family of vehicles using the Tatra engine. Although with Germany's defeat these ambitious plans came to nothing, it was a tribute to the original Czech design that Germany planned to base virtually its entire specialized AFV production on it.

Czech tanks also formed the armoured forces of most of Germany's satellites and the cosmopolitan career of the ČKD/Praga *TNH* continued long after 1945. Czechoslovakia kept the *Hetzer* in production and service and sold 158 to Switzerland as the *PzJg* G13 between 1947 and 1952 and these were in service until 1970. Peru kept *LTP* tanks well into the 1950s. The chassis continued to be used in Sweden as an armoured personnel carrier until 1971, the last in the line of what was one of the most useful designs of armoured fighting vehicle history.

PzKpfw Tiger

Undoubtedly the most famous German tank of the war, the *Tiger*, became to the Allies the symbol of German technological superiority in armoured fighting vehicles. Although by no means invulnerable it was, at the time of its introduction, the most powerfully armed and well-protected tank in the world. To the Allied soldier every German tank became a Tiger, endowed with its offensive and defensive potency and a rather distorted view of German capabilities resulted, as Allied tactical and doctrinal shortcomings could be easily blamed on bigger enemy guns and thicker enemy armour.

The tank which fostered this legend dated back to a 1937 requirement for a 30-ton *Durchbruchswagen* or break-through vehicle. Various designs emerged as ideas changed and finally in May 1941, a month before the invasion of Russia, Hitler demanded a still more powerful tank superior to such heavily armoured vehicles as the French *Char* B and the British Matilda already encountered in the West. The existing plans were enlarged and a year later Henschel and Porsche demonstrated their prototypes.

Trials showed that the Henschel *VK* 4501 design was superior and it was accepted into service as the *PzKpfw* VI *Tiger Ausf* H (*SdKfz* 181). The tank was renamed *PzKpfw Tiger Ausf* E in 1944. It was a relatively conventional vehicle with eight torsion bar suspended interleaved rubber-tyred road wheels each side. This suspension was designed to distribute the heavy weight of the tank as evenly as possible and it gave a very smooth and steady ride

to the tank. Reliability was, however, a problem and from early 1944 new all-steel resilient wheels were introduced which allowed the outside wheels to be deleted. The transmission was an advanced design to cope with the tank's 52-ton weight and a pre-selector gear box was fitted. As the Tiger was too heavy for the normal clutch and brake steering a hydraulic fully regenerative system operated by a driver's wheel was adopted which gave two turning radii in each gear. Control was very light but a price was paid in complexity of maintenance and construction.

The construction of the hull was relatively simple with a single unit welded superstructure in turn welded to the hull. As the tank had been designed before the full lessons of the *T-34* had been learnt, the superstructure armour was not sloped but it made up for this in thickness of protection. The turret, originally developed for the Porsche tank, was also simple and well protected, the sides and rear being formed from a single bent piece of 80-mm armour. It mounted in a heavy mantlet a 56-calibre *KwK* 36 88-mm gun which could penetrate 112 mm of 30 degree armour at 500 yards (457 m) using conventional armour-piercing shot. A machine-gun was fitted co-axially in the mantlet fired by a pedal operated by the gunner. There was another in the right hull-front operated by the radio operator/gunner. The other members of the crew were the driver in the left hull-front and the loader and commander who occupied the turret together with the gunner.

Given its weight the Tiger was a relatively

compact vehicle but its heaviness had disadvantages and both range and speed were very limited. The turret traverse was very low-geared and the gun could only be revolved slowly. Power transverse was fitted but if this failed it took no less than 720 turns of the traversing wheel to get the gun round 360 degrees; this allowed well-handled Allied tanks to put shots into the more vulnerable sides and rear. Wide (725-mm) tracks were fitted to spread the weight although special narrow (520-mm) tracks had to be used for transport by rail to get the tank within the loading gauge. Even with its wide tracks the *Tiger* was too heavy for normal bridges and the first production vehicles were fitted to wade rivers.

Tiger tanks were intended for use in independent three company battalions of 30 tanks allocated to higher Army or Corps HQ for issue in the support role to stiffen various units. This remained the case despite Guderian's intention to make a *Tiger* battalion organic to each Panzer division. This occurred in few

Below: *One of the initial designs that led to the Tiger was the VK 3001(.H) sometimes known as 'Leopard'. When made obsolete by changing requirements two of the four prototypes were lengthened and converted into tank destroyers mounting large 128-mm K 40 guns*
Opposite page, bottom: *This clear rear view of a 1942–3 production Tiger shows off the Feifel air pre-cleaners fitted for the dusty conditions in both Russia and North Africa*

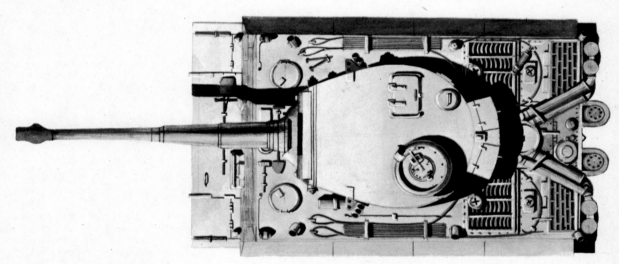

PzKpfw Tiger Ausf E
Weight 54.1 tons (55 tonnes)
Crew five
Armament one 88-mm KwK 36 (L/56) gun with 92 rounds and two 7.92-mm MG 34 machine-guns with 5,700 rounds
Armour hull nose 100 mm, glacis 60 mm, driver's plate 100 mm, sides 60–80 mm, decking and belly 26 mm, tail 82 mm; turret mantlet 110 mm, front 100 mm, sides and rear 80 mm, top 26 mm
Engine one Maybach HL 230 P 45 water-cooled petrol, 694-hp
Speed 23 mph (37 km/h)
Range 62 miles (100 km)
Trench crossing 7 feet 6 inches (2.29 m)
Vertical step 2 feet 7 inches (79 cm)
Fording 4 feet (1.22 m) or with special equipment 13 feet (3.96 m)
Overall length 27 feet 9 inches (8.46 m)
Width wide tracks: 12 feet 3 inches (3.73 m), narrow tracks: 10 feet 4 inches (3.15 m)
Height 9 feet 6 inches (2.9 m)

Above: *A middle production PzKpfw VI Tiger Ausf H, as the tank was originally designated. Note the Feifel air cleaners and the cup like grenade dischargers*

Panzerjager Tiger (P), Elefant
Weight 66.9 tons (68 tonnes)
Crew six
Armament one 88-mm StuK 43/2 (L/71) gun
with 50 rounds
Armour hull nose and driver's plate 100 + 100 mm,
sides 80 mm, decking 30 mm, belly 20 + 30 mm,
tail 80 mm; superstructure front 200 mm, sides
and rear 80 mm, top 30 mm
Engines two Maybach HL 120 TRM V-12 liquid
cooled petrol, 530-hp
Speed 12.5 mph (20 km/h)
Range 95 miles (153 km)
Trench crossing 10 feet 6 inches (3.20 m)
Vertical step 31 inches (78 cm)
Fording 4 feet (1.22 m)
Overall length 26 feet 8 inches (8.13 m)
Width 11 feet 1 inch (3.38 m)
Height 9 feet 10 inches (3.00 m)

Above: The ill-fated Elefant tank destroyer. One of the type's crucial weaknesses is clearly visible, the lack of a hull machine-gun deleted in up-armouring. As can be seen, vision to the rear and sides was very limited and the 88-mm gun had a traverse of only 14° in elevation, 8° in depression and 14° either side. The extra protection was added to the mantlet after the appearance of the initial production vehicles

Army units, the politically influential *Waffen SS* getting priority. *Tiger* tanks were also used with remote control demolition tanks in *Panzer Funklenk Abteilungen* (Radio Controlled Tank Battalions) in the assault role.

With a gun that could defeat the best Allied tank of its time, and frontal armour that could deflect any available Allied anti-tank projectile, the success of the *Tiger* seemed assured. Unfortunately Hitler's desire to see them in action as soon as possible led to fiasco: badly deployed in small quantities in unsuitable terrain, they were overwhelmed in their first offensive action near Leningrad in the autumn of 1942. Misused at Kursk, in July 1943, as a battering ram against mile upon mile of alerted *Pakfront* defences, defeat was on a larger scale. But in defence the *Tiger* showed its great strength and the real legend grew. When firing from camouflaged positions, using tracked mobility to move from one to the other and supported by other tanks or small groups of infantry the *Tiger* took a great deal of stalking and absorbed a disproportionate amount of Allied strength. On one famous occasion, in July 1944, a single *Tiger* of the 501 *Waffen SS* Heavy Tank Battalion held up the British Seventh Armoured Division, the Desert Rats, knocking out 25 armoured vehicles.

However, as time went on the *Tiger*'s superiority began to be eroded by new Allied tank

Above: *After the Kursk disaster several Elefant tank destroyers fell into Russian hands like this example here. The burnt superstructure is evidence of attack with flame-thrower or 'Molotov cocktail' petrol bombs. In action a wooden plank was wired to the rear on which German infantrymen could ride though at considerable risk*

Below: *The Tiger tanks of the 501st Heavy Tank Battalion were sent to Tunisia in January 1943 to reinforce the Axis position there. Although providing much useful support they did not prove completely invulnerable as shown by this example which has been blown on its side, probably by an Allied bomb or mine*

Sturmpanzer VI, Sturmtiger
Weight 66.9 tons (68 tonnes)
Crew five or six
Armament one 380-mm Raketenwerfer 61 with
12 rounds and one 7.92-mm MG 34 machine-gun
Armour superstructure front 150 mm, sides and
rear 84 mm, top 40 mm
Overall length 20 feet 8½ inches (6.30 m)
Height (with crane) 11 feet 4 inches (3.45 m)
Other details as PzKpfw IV Tiger Ausf E tank

Right: *This is one of the ten production Sturmtiger built on a 1944 production Ausf E tank
chassis with the later type wheel arrangement.
The prototype Sturmtiger had a similar suspension
to that of the tank previously illustrated. The
new arrangement placed a lower strain on the
wheel bearings and was less prone to packing
with mud or ice. The crane was to assist in loading
the 761-lb (345-kg) 380-mm rocket projectiles.
Their maximum range was over 6,000 yards
(5,500 m) but accuracy was not very great and
Sturmtiger was meant to be used at much closer
distances*

guns which had sufficient performance to penetrate the *Tiger*'s armour at average combat ranges (500 to 1,000 yards or 457 m to 914 m). Production was gradually phased out, and finally ceased in August 1944. In all 1,355 had been built, surprisingly few considering their tremendous reputation.

Although not selected for quantity production the *Tiger* offered by Dr Ferdinand Porsche, the *VK 4501* (P), saw limited service as a heavy assault gun chassis with the long (70-calibre) 88-mm *PaK* 43/2 – a more powerful gun than that of the Tiger tank. Eighty-five chassis were converted by Alkett and they emerged as the *Panzerjäger Tiger* (P) (*SdKfz* 184); originally called *Ferdinand* after their designer they later received the official name *Elefant*. To make it more suitable for its task the chassis was changed in layout. The driver and radio operator remained in the front, the former fighting compartment now contained the engines – two standard Maybach 120 TR units – and a large fighting compartment was rear-mounted to minimize the long gun's overhang. The suspension remained on the Porsche principle with six large, steel-rimmed road wheels each side, in pairs mounted on three horizontal torsion bars. Drive was transmitted to rear sprockets via a Siemens Schuckert electric generator and two electric drive motors; steering was hydro-pneumatically assisted. Armour was increased to an extraordinary level, an extra 100-mm armour plate being bolted to the hull front, already armoured to this thickness. The superstructure received 200-mm armour at the front, the rest being armoured to 80 mm.

The *Elefant* was a formidable, if specialized, tank destroyer. Great things were expected of it and two army Tank Destroyer Battalions, 653 and 654 were re-equipped each with three companies of twelve *Elefant* with an HQ Company of two extra vehicles and a *PzKpfw* III. But its first major offensive role at Kursk was a disaster. Employed as an assault vehicle, to lead the infantry through the Soviet defences, its lack of flexibility or close-in defence capability was fatal. The *Elefant* is usually remembered for this failure but this was as much a product of misuse as intrinsic defects. As a long range tank killer it was supreme for its day, totally impervious frontally to enemy fire and capable of knocking out a *T-34* at three miles (4·83 km) in open country. The lessons of Kursk were learnt and those which were salvaged from the battlefield were fitted with machine-guns in the right hull-front. The two battalions served later in Russia and Italy, where they were used more prudently as mobile anti-tank pillboxes. Nevertheless, they remained awkward machines to operate, proving too heavy to be very mobile especially on Italian roads in bad weather; reliability and spare parts remained a problem and many had to be destroyed to escape capture.

The spectacular *Sturmtiger* assault howitzer originated from a requirement for a 210-mm assault howitzer to destroy heavy buildings which the Russians had converted into fortresses; no suitable weapon was available and a 380-mm heavy rocket launcher, developed as an anti-submarine weapon for the German Navy, was mounted in a Henschel *Tiger* chassis. A prototype was built in October 1943 but production only began at Alkett in August 1944 when ten standard chassis could be spared for re-working.

Sturmtiger was a clumsy vehicle, almost as heavy and certainly as specialized as *Elefant* and by the time it came into service there was little real function for a mobile assault rocket launcher as Germany's armies were on the defensive, not storming through Russian cities. Its fuel consumption, two gallons per mile, was even higher than the *Tiger* tanks, not very suitable for a country short of fuel with its synthetic oil plants coming under increasing air attack. *Sturmtiger* assault howitzers were committed to battle individually but were soon knocked out or captured.

Not many *Tiger* tanks were exported but Italy received 36 which were repossessed when she changed sides. Spain also managed to acquire a few as part of arms deals with Germany.

Below: *A captured Sturmtiger with an example of its ammunition in front of it. The spin-stabilized 761-lb (345-kg) rocket came in two versions, a normal high explosive and a hollow charge*

PzKpfw Panther

In early October 1941 the Fourth *Panzer* Division, part of Guderian's recently renamed Second *Panzer* Army was severely mauled by the new Soviet *T*-34 tanks, encountered in significant numbers for the first time, near Mzensk. Tank losses were heavy and Guderian asked for a commission of representatives from all sides of German tank development to be sent to the front to report on the situation. Ideas of building a simple copy of the *T*-34 were soon dismissed due to difficulties in copying the Soviet aluminium diesel engine and other problems with materials. Daimler Benz and MAN were therefore contracted to produce a new German *VK* 3002 design to regain technological superiority.

Detailed specifications were issued in January 1942 with the following parameters: weight 35 tons, armament a 75-mm gun and co-axial machine-gun, maximum hull armour 60 mm and turret armour 100 mm and speed 37 mph (60 km/h). The design was also to include all the features of the *T*-34 that made it such a formidable opponent: sloped armour which increased the effective thickness of any given plate, large road wheels to improve the ride and a long powerful gun overhanging the chassis, a feature which German designers had been wary of.

In April designs were submitted by Daimler Benz and MAN. Hitler preferred the former's but a special committee of the OKH's Army Weapons Department, set up to deal with the problem, came down in favour of the more conventional MAN design with a petrol engine, front drive sprockets. interleaved suspension and a turret set back to minimize the overhang problem. The hull was a single welded unit with

strengthened edges and well-sloped 55 degree 60-mm glacis armour. It was hoped that 250 *PzKpfw* V *Panther* (*SdKfz* 171) would be in service by May 1943; in September, the month that the first two pilot models appeared, Hitler raised this target to 600.

Tests showed that the design was overweight and underpowered but the first 20 vehicles designated *Ausf* A (but not to be confused with the later *Ausf* A mass produced after the battle of Kursk) were built to the prototype design in order to get production under way. To increase power a new HL 230 engine was fitted to subsequent production vehicles (*Ausf* D) together with a specially designed AK7 200 synchromesh gearbox and regenerative steering system to cope with the extra weight. Armour thickness was increased, in accordance with Hitler's order of June 1942, to 80 mm and the turret cupola was moved over to the right to simplify production. A new double-baffle gun muzzle brake began to be fitted.

In January the first production *Panther* appeared from both MAN and Daimler Benz – the latter having been brought in to meet the ambitious production schedule. By February MNH were also in the programme and Henschel and Demag joined later. In early 1943 *Ausf* A vehicles were officially reclassified D1 and production vehicles D2 while from May *Schürtzen* began to be fitted to guard the gap between the track top and the superstructure side. By that month 324 *Panther* tanks were in service.

The modifications to the *Panther Ausf* D2 were far from sufficient to solve its mechanical difficulties: the HL 230 engine was prone to

overheating and catching fire; the final drive was also a particular weakness, closely followed by the rest of the transmission and the steering. The increased weight (44 tons) also put extra stress on the rim bolts holding on the tyres which often necessitated much time consuming wheel removal to get at the offending failure. All this reflected insufficient development time but, despite Guderian's doubts, Hitler insisted that the *Panther* should be put into service as soon as possible, notably in time for the big armoured offensive at Kursk, Operation *Zitadelle*, which was delayed until July 1943 so that the new tanks could be used. Not surprisingly their *début* was inauspicious. Of the 200 *Panther* tanks in Hoth's Fourth *Panzer* Army, 160 were out of action by the end of the first day, and, nine days later, only 43 were in German hands. Many had broken down between the railheads and the front, others on the battlefield where, as they could not be easily towed, they had had to be left.

By the time the Kursk offensive was abandoned a new *Panther* model, rather confusingly called the *Ausf* A was in production, with a proper ball-mounted hull machine-gun and a better protected turret with new cupola. To ease production and in order to help mitigate the effects of the weight problem more tyre bolts were used in the wheels, 24 instead of 16.

Below: *The fate of many a Panther is exemplified by this burnt out Ausf A; neither its extra camouflage nor well-sloped armour has saved it from Allied firepower*

Opposite page, right: *A Panther Ausf G – note the new shape of the superstructure sides*

PzKpfw V Panther Ausf G
Weight 44.8 tons (45.5 tonnes)
Crew five
Armament one 75-mm KwK 42 (L/70) gun with
79 rounds and two 7.92-mm MG 34 machine-guns
with 4,500 rounds
Armour hull front 80 mm, sides 50 mm, tail 40 mm,
decking 15 mm, belly 20 + 13 mm; turret front 120–
110 mm, sides and rear 45 mm, top 15 mm
Engine one Maybach HL 230 P 30 V-12 liquid-
cooled petrol, 690-hp
Speed 34 mph (55 km/h)
Range 110 miles (177 km)
Trench crossing 6 feet 3 inches (1.9 m)
Vertical step 3 feet (90 cm)
Fording 4 feet 7 inches (1.4 m)
Overall length 29 feet 1 inch (8.86 m)
Width 10 feet 10 inches (3.30 m)
Height 9 feet 8 inches (2.95 m)

*Below: This Ausf G Panther is identified as such
by its new-style upward hinging hatches and the
deletion of the driver's vision visor. A brown
camouflage scheme has been applied over the
basic sand yellow which was the standard finish
for tanks leaving the factories in 1943–4*

Jagdpanther
Weight 44.8 tons (45.5 tonnes)
Crew six
Armament one 88-mm PaK 43/3 (L/71) with
60 rounds and one 7.92-mm MG 34 machine-gun
with 600 rounds
Armour front 80 mm, mantlet 120 mm, sides
40–50 mm, decking 17 mm, belly 20 + 13 mm,
tail 40 mm
Speed 28.5 mph (46 km/h)
Range 100 miles (160 km)
Overall length 33 feet 3 inches (10.m)
Height 8 feet 11 inches (2.72 m)
Other details as PzKpfw V Panther Ausf G tank

Left: *A late model Jagdpanther with two-piece
gun barrel and simplified heavy bolted-on mantlet
collar. Schürtzen are fitted and the excellent
ballistic shape of the vehicle's armour can be seen.
Grey camouflage schemes became increasingly
common once more from late 1944. Jagdpanther
was a formidable vehicle; on July 30th 1944 three
from the 654 heavy AT battalion knocked out over
half a squadron of 15 British Churchills in a little
over a minute*

Ausf Ds were modified with extra bolts put in between the existing 16, making 32 in all. Although the engine became a little more reliable with extra cooling fans, improved bearings and other modifications, transmission failures remained endemic. New *Ausf* A turrets were fitted to *Ausf* D hulls by Henschel who kept the older chassis in production until November 1943. Altogether 1,768 *Panthers* were produced in 1943. Further modifications were planned to produce the *Panther* II *Ausf* F to simplify production and improve reliability but production was not quite under way when the war ended.

The need in 1944 was for as many tanks as possible of existing design in the front-line and some of the innovations of the proposed *Panther* II were added to the standard *Panther* in early 1944 to produce the *PzKpfw Panther Ausf* G. (The term *PzKpfw* V was now dropped.) To simplify production further the design of the sides of the tank were modified to make the rear stowage areas integral with the hull. The hull sides were also increased to 50-mm armour and the driver acquired a rotating periscope. Late production vehicles had a modified mantlet with thicker bottom to prevent the deflection of enemy rounds into the thin deck armour. In the last vehicles constructed all-steel resilient wheels were fitted which finally solved one dimension of the weight problem and the improved AK7-400 gearbox was also adopted. A progressive

Below: *A knocked out Jagdpanther being inspected by an American soldier. This vehicle has the 'clean' gun barrel but the later style mantlet collar. Note the penetration made through the wheels. Jagdpanthers were vulnerable to such flanking shots and also to track damage caused by high-explosive fire*

feature introduced in action just before the end of the war was the use of infra-red night fighting equipment which enabled the crews to engage targets at night up to 547 yards (500 m) away.

During 1944 and 1945 over 3,740 *Panther* tanks were produced, more than any other single type of German tank in this period. It provided a numerous and powerful supplement to the *PzKpfw* IV as the major battle tank of the *Panzer* divisions. Each division was supposed to contain one battalion of *Panther* tanks together with one of *PzKpfw* IV but as usual the *élite Waffen SS* tended to get priority.

Ausf A and G vehicles played a prominent part in the large-scale defensive tank battles in Normandy. Here mobility was less important than their formidable frontal protection and 3,068 fps (935 m/s) gun that could penetrate over 120 mm of 30-degree plate at 1,000 yards (914 m). Only crushing Allied air and numerical superiority prevented this technological advantage becoming decisive strategically.

The *Panther* had a small number of special versions, the most famous was the *Jagdpanther* (Hunting Panther) tank destroyer. This was developed in 1943 as a well-protected mobile mount for the formidable *PaK* 43 88-mm gun with its 3,708 fps (1,130 m/s) muzzle velocity and which could penetrate 226 mm of 30 degree armour at 500 yards (457 m). *Nashorn* was too lightly protected and *Elefant* too expensive, complex and vulnerable for the task, so it was decided to use the *Panther* chassis with a low sloped front superstructure. The gun was fitted in the frontal plate with 11-degree traverse to each side, 8-degree elevation and 14-degree depression and a machine-gun was fitted in the right hull front to prevent a repetition of the Kursk débacle. A crew of six was needed: commander,

gunner, wireless operator/machine-gunner, driver and two loaders for the heavy, clumsy ammunition. First called *Panzerjäger Panther* (*SfKfz* 173) it received from Hitler the designation *Jagdpanther* in 1944.

Production began in December 1943 and MIAG had it well under way by May using *Ausf* G chassis with an improved AK7-400 gearbox to take the extra weight. The vehicles were issued to special tank destroyer battalions composed of 30 *Jagdpanther* which were kept under central army control. It was intended to build 150 *Jagdpanther* a month but an increasingly bombed and starved German industry could not keep up and only 382 were eventually completed. Several other *Panther*-based vehicles saw service: the demand for heavy recovery vehicles after Kursk resulted in the *Bergepanzer Panther* or *Bergepanther* recovery vehicle (*SdKfz* 179); *Ausf* D, A and G vehicles were converted to *Befehlspanzer* (command tanks) and there was also an artillery observation post vehicle or *Beobachtungspanzer* (*SdKfz* 172).

Some 5,508 examples of the *Panther* tank were built in all. Although considered excessively large by the Ministry of Armaments and retaining mechanical problems which were never entirely ironed out, it was probably the best all round German tank of the war, not too heavy but well-armoured and armed. Its complexity hindered mass production but two could be built in as many man-hours as one *Tiger* and, in the 1944 rationalization plan, it was hoped to concentrate on it and the *Panther* II as the main battle tanks of the 1945 German Army. A total of 400 a month was planned but this was far beyond the capacity of German industry, even though 132 *Ausf* Gs were still produced as late as February 1945.

PzKpfw Tiger Ausf B

In August 1942 specifications were issued for a modified *Tiger* tank incorporating the latest sloped armour of the *T-34* and *Panther*, increased protection and the longer 71-calibre 88-mm gun. It was hoped that this would keep German tanks ahead of any future Soviet designs in the gun/armour race. Both Porsche and Henschel were again asked to tender and the former produced modified *VK 4502 (P)* versions of his earlier *Tiger (P)*. Interest was shown in a version with electric drive and rear mounted 88-mm gun, and, with Porsche this time sure of a production order, construction of turrets was begun. But the need for copper, a scarce commodity in blockaded Germany, for the electric transmission resulted in the Henschel *VK 4503 (H)* design being chosen for service.

Ordered in January 1943 the first *PzKpfw VI Tiger II* or *Ausf B* (*SdKfz 182*) did not appear until the end of the year due to the need for close liaison with MAN in order to standardize as many components as possible with the proposed *Panther II* – the *Tiger II*, for example used the same engine as late model *Panther* tanks. Suspension was on the classic German principle with conventional torsion bars but the arrangement of wheels was slightly altered compared with the earlier *Tiger*; the interleaved system was abandoned due to the difficulty of access to the inner wheels and the tendency of these arrangements to freeze or jam and the nine sets of double bogie wheels were set merely to overlap. Resilient steel wheels were also employed to improve reliability. As with the older

Tiger two sets of tracks were provided: one for action and the other for transport to minimize the vehicle's width.

Production was under way by February 1944 when the first eight vehicles were produced by Henschel side by side with 95 standard *Tiger Ausf Es*. It was the intention to produce 145 *Tiger II Ausf Bs* per month by 1945 but this proved impossible and the total production run was only 484. The first 50 vehicles carried the turret designed for the Porsche tank, the others had the proper Henschel turret with its heavier armour and squared-off front which prevented shots being deflected down into the hull. Some Porsche turreted vehicles and all the Henschel turreted tanks had a two-piece gun barrel which allowed differential wear to be exploited in replacement of parts.

Tiger Ausf B, known to its own side as *Königstiger* and to the English-speaking world as Royal or King Tiger, was a formidable and huge vehicle. It was at once the heaviest, most thickly protected and most powerfully armed battle tank to see service in any numbers during the war. Its armour would do justice to a modern main battle tank and its gun had a muzzle velocity of 3,220 fps (981 m/s) and could penetrate 182 mm of 30-degree armour at 500 yards (457 m). This was more than enough to deal with the heaviest Soviet JS IIs. But a price had to be paid in size, weight and reliability. Hull length was 23 feet 8½ inches (7·22 m) and height was also greater. Most important, weight was also increased, by over ten tons. Although, sur-

prisingly, this did not affect performance 'on paper', speed and radius of action actually being slightly increased, power/weight ratio, manoeuvrability and ground pressure all suffered. Also, inevitably, reliability was a problem with a highly stressed engine and transmission.

These drawbacks did not matter too much in defensive battles but it was a significant drawback in, for example, the Ardennes offensive. Indeed, although *Tiger IIs* were available to Obersturmführer (Lieutenant-Colonel) Jochen Peiper he chose *PzKpfw IVs* and *Panther* tanks to lead his *Kampfgruppe* that spearheaded the advance of First *SS Panzer* Division. The *Tiger II* had made its combat *début* on the Eastern Front in May 1944 and was in service in France by August of the same year. It was allocated in the same way as the *Tiger I* being either kept in independent battalions or being formed into the tank regiments of privileged *Panzer* divisions. With such a small production run the *Tiger II* was never a common tank and, although the previously mentioned Ardennes offensive is usually associated with it, there were comparatively few in action.

Opposite page, right: *A Tiger Ausf B with standard Henschel turret. These vehicles were used, to a limited extent, in the closing months of the war only being employed in any numbers in the Ardennes and in the defence of Budapest in late 1944 and early 1945*

Below: *One of the first 50 Royal Tiger tanks with Porsche turret, knocked out in Normandy*

PzKpfw Tiger Ausf B
Weight 68.7 tons (69.4 tonnes)
Crew five
Armament one 88-mm KwK 43 (L/71) gun with
80 rounds and two 7.92-mm MG 34 machine-
guns with 5,850 rounds
Armour hull nose 100 mm, glacis 150 mm, sides
and tail 80 mm, decking 40 mm; turret front
185 mm, sides and rear 80 mm, top 44 mm
Engine one Maybach HL 230 P 30 V-12 liquid-
cooled petrol, 600-hp
Speed 23.6 mph (38 km/h)
Range 68.4 miles (110 km)
Trench crossing 8 feet 2 inches (2.5 m)
Vertical step 2 feet 9½ inches (85 cm)
Fording 5 feet 3 inches (1.6 m)
Overall length 33 feet 8 inches (10.26 m)
Width wide tracks: 12 feet 3½ inches (4.72 m),
narrow tracks: 10 feet 8¾ inches (3.27 m)
Height 10 feet 1½ inches (3.08 m)

If the Royal Tiger was the most powerful tank of the war then its tank destroyer derivative *Jagdtiger* (*SdKfz* 186) was the most powerful armoured vehicle. It was German policy to build a limited-traverse mounting of the 'next size gun up' on any given tank chassis and the Royal Tiger was no exception. A lengthened hull was used with a large fixed central superstructure armoured to the extraordinary frontal thickness of 250 mm and mounting a 55-calibre 128-mm *PaK* 80 – a weapon which could out-range any other tank gun and penetrate any other AFV. Earlier models mounted the shorter 128-mm *PaK* 44 and some had to make do with the *Jagdpanther*'s 88-mm *PaK* 43/3. The tank's machine-gun in the hull front was retained and a grenade launcher was also fitted, as in the tank, to deter stalkers.

The first mock-up appeared in October 1943; 150 were ordered but only 70 were completed by the end of the war. The close connection between the plant – Neibelüngenwerke – and the designer enabled Dr Porsche to tinker with the design. One *Jagdtiger* was fitted with a Porsche type suspension with eight overlapping wheels instead of nine; this vehicle may also have been the *Jagdtiger* experimentally fitted with a Porsche *SLa* 16 (Type 212) 700-hp diesel engine. Neither of these developments went further due to the need to concentrate on existing designs if any vehicles were to be built at all. A more powerful engine would at least have alleviated the *Jagdtiger*'s greatest drawback – its extra-

ordinary weight of over 70½ tons, more than any other AFV that has ever seen widespread service in any army. This created severe tactical problems as the *Jagdtiger* was impossible to operate on anything but strong roads and the hardest ground and its practical maximum road speed was also very slow, no more than seven to nine mph (11 to 14 km/h).

The *Jagdtiger* equipped independent tank destroyer battalions, usually those of the *Waffen SS*. They were used as infantry support vehicles and as stiffeners in the *Panzer* forces used in the Ardennes offensive but their lack of mobility was a severe drawback and they were most suitable for the final last ditch stands against the Allied forces closing into Germany. Impenetrable to Allied fire, the *Jagdtiger* provided a formidable static anti-tank defence.

There were two other versions of the *Tiger* II *Ausf* B. One, the *Panzerbefehlswagen* command vehicle, was a normal tank with extra radio equipment added and armament stowage decreased in the usual manner; few were produced. The other, the largest of the family of weapons carriers, had *Tiger* II chassis with two extra bogie wheels fitted with a large protected rear superstructure to carry a dismountable 170-mm gun or a 210-mm howitzer. A prototype was almost completed when the war ended. After the war some *Tiger* II tanks served with the French army until being expanded as targets.

The massive proportions of the *Tiger* II series reflected Hitler's enthusiasm for large

AFVs and there were plans for even larger vehicles. In 1942 he had given personal authorization to Porsche to develop a huge 185-ton *Maus* (Mouse) tank with 200-mm armour and an armament of one 128-mm gun with co-axial 75-mm. This led the Army Weapons Office to look for a slightly less impractical design of 'super tank'. At first it was hoped to build a bigger version of *Tiger* II developed by Krupp as the *VK* 7001 (K) called *Tiger-Maus* or *Löwe* (Lion). A model was built showing a redesigned hull with rear-mounted 128-mm armed turret and steeply-sloped armour. This was eventually cancelled and efforts concentrated on the development of the largest of a planned *E* (*Entwicklung* – development) series of standardized tanks. Adler developed the 140-ton *E-100* with a suspension based on the *Tiger* II but with helical springs instead of torsion bars, and its main armament was increased to 150-mm calibre. One prototype petrol-engined *Maus* was built and another with a diesel engine.

Although super-tank projects had soon to be downgraded much time and energy were wasted on what had been described by Porsche himself as mere mobile fortifications. Even less rational were plans for a 1,500-ton tank with one 800-mm gun, two 150-mm weapons and 250-mm armour powered by four U-Boat engines! Such a land monitor would have been the final monument to the German failure to understand that practicality and serviceability were of greater importance than mere technological virtue.

Jagdtiger
Weight 70.6 tons (7.7 tonnes)
Crew six
Armament one 128-mm PaK 80 (L/55) gun
with 38 rounds and one MG 34 machine-gun
with 2,925 rounds
Armour superstructure front 250 mm, sides and
rear 80 mm, top 40 mm
Overall length 35 feet (10.66 m)
Height 9 feet 3 inches (2.82 m)
Other details as Tiger Ausf B tank

*Opposite page: A battalion of normal production
Royal Tigers parade late in 1944. Such pictures
made good propaganda but belied Germany's true
armoured strength at this time. The two piece gun
barrel and 'Zimmerit' anti magnetic-mine paste
are clearly visible on the commander's vehicle.
Note how deeply the heavy vehicles have sunk
into the ground*
*Left: Not even massive armour and firepower
could hold out for ever. This Jagdtiger has been
used as a dug in pill box before being overwhelmed
by American firepower*
*Below: The spectacular Jagdtiger, the most
powerful service AFV of the war, did not see a
great deal of action, only being available in very
limited quantities by the end of the war*

ITALY

The Italian armoured forces in World War II fought well within the limitations of their inferior and often unreliable equipment and essentially conservative principles. In 1926 a separate *Corpo Carristi* (Armoured Corps) was formed and the next year its 100 Fiat 3000 tanks (machine-gun armed modifications of the Renault FT) were organized into a five-battalion *Reggimento Carri Armati* (Army Tank Regiment). Although 80 more Model 30 3000s were built with 37-mm guns, the small Carden Loyd tankette (later modified and designated the *L* 3) seemed the best means of quickly boosting Italy's armoured reserves, given her limited industrial capacity. From 1933 developed versions were procured in large quantities from Fiat-Ansaldo. They were allocated to cavalry groups and to infantry support battalions, re-organized in 1936 into four administrative infantry tank regiments. This combination of technology and organization proved adequate in Ethiopia in 1934–5, but not in Spain against more sophisticated opposition from anti-tank guns and Soviet-made tanks.

From 1936 the Italians began to toy with the idea of larger armoured formations to maximize the power of the projected, heavier breakthrough tank eventually designated M 11/39. First *Brigata Motomeccanizzata* (Mechanized Brigade) was formed from a two-company tankette battalion, a light infantry (*bersaglieri*) regiment, an artillery battery and engineer platoon. The next year this was enlarged to form two *brigate corazzate* (armoured brigades), each with a new regiment of three to four tankette battalions, a motorized *bersaglieri* regiment, anti-tank and anti-aircraft guns and engineers.

Although the organization of the brigade, like that of the French *DCR*, was essentially traditional and reflected the conservative doctrine of Italian high command, the Italians did eventually begin to take notice of German theories of tank warfare. In 1939, after air-supported mechanized operations in Albania, exercises in *guerra di rapido corso* were carried out in Italy. In these Second *Brigata Corazzata* took part, expanded with field artillery and extra support units into the 132nd *Ariete* Armoured Division. First Armoured Brigade was re-formed on similar lines as the 131st *Centauro* and by the end of the year the 133rd *Littorio* had been converted from an infantry division.

Italy had about 1,500 tanks available in 1940, of which 100 were new *M* 11/39 mediums. A few were old 3000s and the rest *L* 3 tankettes. The first vehicles to see service were in independent battalions in southern France, East Africa and the Western Desert. In the last-named theatre most armour was eventually formed into two four-battalion Groups and by December 1940 into a Special Armoured Brigade, but the tanks still tended to be deployed piecemeal. Moreover, the general inferiority of most of them to British tanks and armoured cars made the Italians cautious and the Allied victory more certain.

Quantity production of *M* 13/40s, more heavily armed and armoured modern tanks, was only just getting under way, and these were rushed to North Africa in individual battalions. Even when coherent divisions were available, albeit still largely *L* 3 equipped, they were often dispersed in action. *Ariete* was the first to be completely equipped with modern *M* 13/40s and used by Rommel in his first offensive. *Centauro* was used piecemeal in Greece during the unsuccessful invasion in 1940 and again in Yugoslavia with *Littorio*. The latter was part of a mechanized corps with two unmotorized infantry divisions, so the armour soon outran its support. This combination of incompatible units was due to both shortage of equipment, and, one suspects, lack of proper understanding of the true principles of mechanized operations. It was a common Italian failing. Only in August 1941 was a proper Mobile Army Corps (*Corpo d'armata di Manovra*) formed from a union of the *Ariete* with the *Trieste* motorized infantry division,

and an armoured corps reconnaissance unit.

When it was decided to transfer the *Littorio* to Africa at the end of 1941 its establishment was revised to a three-battalion *M* 13/40 regiment, a *bersaglieri* regiment, an artillery regiment (including two groups of the new *Semovente* 75-mm assault guns), two desert patrol units, support elements and extra reconnaissance grouping of a *bersaglieri* battalion and group of *L* 6/40 light tanks. But the units never fought together: the infantry were sunk in transit and other troops were used to reinforce units which had already been in action. The *Ariete* was also re-structured along the new lines at the beginning of 1942 but both divisions were destroyed at Alamein.

The *Centauro*, also organized along the new lines with an armoured grouping of *L* 6/40s and *Semovente* 47/32s, was sent to Africa in confusion in late 1942 and was never re-assembled. Its name was taken by an *ad hoc* grouping of some of its elements with the survivors of other divisions. After combat with Allied forces it was destroyed with the Axis collapse in Tunisia.

The Italian failure seems both administrative and logistical for by 1942 tank production was well under way. Considering Italy's limited industrial capacity it was a considerable achievement to produce over 2,000 medium tanks between 1940 and 1943, as well as light tanks and *Semoventi*. The weakness lay in the quality of the vehicles; Italian tanks fell behind in the technological race. Plans for Italian production of German tanks, first *PzKpfw* III *Ausf* J and then *PzKpfw* IV and *Panther*, came to nothing, although 36 *Tigers* were supplied in 1941 and some German *PzKpfw* IVs fought in Italian hands in Russia. There were also plans to produce a virtual copy of the British Crusader, the *Carro Armato Celere Sahariano*, for desert warfare but this was only a prototype by the time of Axis defeat in North Africa.

The major new Italian tank project, the *P* 26/40, began in 1940 to provide a heavy fourth com-

pany in every *M* 13/40 battalion but was badly delayed. The tank finally emerged as a 26-ton diesel-powered vehicle with 50-mm armour and 34-calibre 75-mm gun. But by September 1943 and Italy's surrender, only 24 had been built out of an order of 1,000 and these were taken and used by the Germans. Production of existing mediums had already stopped in March to concentrate on Semoventi.

In April 1943 a new 135th *Ariete* II Armoured Cavalry Division was formed with an establishment of an armoured regiment of three battalions (one company of *M* 15/42s and two of *Semoventi* 75/18 in each), a motorized cavalry regiment, two regiments of artillery (one completely *Semovente*-equipped) and an SP anti-tank battalion, with *Semovente*-equipped armoured grouping and support echelons. After some brief fighting against the Germans this unit was disbanded, as was the *Centauro* II division formed from two Blackshirt units, the *Legionario* motorized regiment and *Leonessa* armoured group. This was originally grouped with the 131st Tank Regiment (equipped with *L* 3s, *L* 6/40s and French R-35s) artillery and other support as the M Division. The 131st were sent on their own to Sicily and, when Mussolini was overthrown, the Fascist units, whose loyalty was in doubt, were joined by a reliable *bersaglieri* regiment and medium tank battalion. With the surrender, the army units briefly fought the Germans, but *Leonessa* and another Blackshirt armoured group, *Leoncello*, continued to fight the Allies in the Army of the Socialist Italian Republic.

Left: *A company of M 13/40 tanks pictured in Cyrenaica during Rommel's final drive on Egypt*

L 3 and L 6 Light Tanks

The *L* 3 and *L* 6 Light tanks were developed from four Carden Loyd Mark VI tankettes originally purchased from Britain in 1929. The tankette was re-designated *Carro Veloce* (fast tank) 29, and 21 were completed under licence by Fiat-Ansaldo. The first vehicles were vulnerable, semi-open and armed with a single machine-gun. By 1931 development of a fully-enclosed, more heavily-armoured *CV 3* was under way and this was accepted for service as the *CV 33*.

The new tankette was designed to operate as a battle tank and weight was almost doubled from the 1.7 tons of the *CV 29*. Construction was of riveted armour plates and the suspension was of an improved Carden Loyd type with, each side, two elliptically sprung, rubber-tyred three-wheel bogie assemblies and a single unsprung wheel at the rear. Drive was from the transverse rear-mounted engine through a gearbox in front of the driver to the front sprockets. Steering was by levers and epicyclic clutch.

The driver sat on the right and the commander/gunner on the left. In the first two prototypes the latter worked a 6.5-mm Revelli Fiat water-cooled machine-gun but from the third prototype this was replaced with a lighter,

similar calibre air-cooled Fiat Type 14 weapon. In 1935 the slightly modified *CV 33* Series II mounted two 8-mm Fiat Model 14/35 machine guns and the older vehicles were altered to the new standard. The original plans for a 37-mm armed *CV 33* never materialized.

The tankettes were deployed as *carri d'assalto* in infantry support battalions or as *carri veloci* in cavalry groups with 43 vehicles in each. There were three companies/squadrons each of 13 tankettes, three platoons of four plus a commander. From 1935 the tank battalions included new specialized versions. A flame-thrower tank (*carro lanciafiamme*) was developed to enhance infantry support capabilities. The flame-gun had a range of 50–100 yards (46–92 metres) while its fuel was carried at first in an armoured box over the engine compartment, and later, more safely, in an armoured trailer. One platoon in each tank company was eventually equipped with these. A *carro radio* was also issued to each tank company commander with a large circular type aerial on the left-hand side and battery compartments mounted over the engine. Armament was sometimes deleted in order to fit a map table. Radio tanks were not issued to the Cavalry until

1940 when the *gruppo squadroni* went on to a five-squadron establishment, one a command squadron with five *carri radio*. Machine-gun ammunition trailers, in use by the tank battalions for some time, were then issued to the cavalry.

A spectacular modification, produced only in limited quantities, was the *CV 33/II Pasarella* bridgelayer developed by the Engineers. This was a winch-fitted tankette which towed a seven-metre (23 feet) bridge in sections on a trailer. When the battlefield was reached the bridge was assembled and pushed on a wheel assembly to the obstacle on which it was lowered into position. As far as is known this was not used in action. Recovery vehicles fitted with towing equipment (and without armament) were built.

In 1936, after 760 *CV 33*s a new version of the tankette appeared, the *CV 35*. This had a bolted superstructure, improved vision equipment and other modifications. There were both flame-thrower and radio versions. From 1938 new 8-mm Breda Model 38 machine-guns began to be fitted to both new and old vehicles and that same year the tank was redesignated *Carro Armato L 3/33* and *L 3/35* (*L* for *leggero* – light; 3 for the tonnage and 33 and 35 for the year of

Below: *An L 3/35 Lf shows off its spectacular capabilities during the siege of Tobruk in 1941. These flame-thrower tankettes were widely used for infantry support*

introduction). Tests the previous year with a *CV 33* fitted with a new superstructure and turret-mounted 20-mm gun were not followed up and neither were tests with a 47-mm gun tank destroyer on the *L 3* chassis in 1939–40, but some *L 3*s were fitted with an 8-mm Fiat or Breda machine-gun on an AA mount and saw service thus in small quantities.

About 2,500 standard *L 3*s were built. Almost 500 saw service during the conquest of Ethiopia where, against unsophisticated opposition, their terrain-crossing ability stood them in good stead. One battalion, followed later by a second, was sent to support the Italian volunteer division in the Spanish Civil War but here, against anti-tank guns and Soviet-made tanks, the story was different, and success more difficult to attain.

Despite these lessons, when Italy entered World War II the overwhelming majority of her tanks remained *L 3*s, including most of those equipping the armoured regiments of the three armoured divisions. *L 3*s fought with Italian forces on all fronts: in France, North Africa (where the long distances showed up reliability problems), the Balkans and even Russia. Despite attempts to up-gun some with 20-mm Solothurn anti-tank guns *L 3*s were hopelessly outclassed against any real opposition. Some, however, were still in first-line Italian service in 1943 and were used by the Germans after the Italian surrender; while both the Greek Army and the Yugoslav partisans used them against their former owners.

The *L 3* sold widely before the war to Afghanistan, Albania, Austria, Bolivia, Brazil, Bulgaria, China, Hungary, Iraq and Salvador. A special export version with large road wheels, torsion bar suspension and a 13.2-mm Madsen machine-gun was also sold to Brazil.

The other type of light tank to see service with the Italian Army in World War II was the *L 6/40*. The design dated back to 1936 when a larger and more heavily-armed five-ton, two-man tank was developed by Fiat-Ansaldo as a possible *L 3* replacement. At first the *L 3* layout was followed with a 37-mm gun in the hull but the next example also had a turret with twin 8-mm machine-guns and a third prototype had a turret-mounted 37-mm. The suspension was on the torsion bar principle with two sets of double-wheel bogies each side.

The Italian army were, at first, uninterested and the design was improved with exports only in mind, though after tests it was ordered to replace *L 3*s in cavalry formations. The new tank which appeared in 1940 was slightly up in weight (hence the designation *L 6/40*) with an improved suspension. Prototypes had a turret with a 37-mm gun or twin machine-guns, but the production version mounted an automatic Breda 20-mm gun and co-axial machine-gun. The same turret was also mounted on the *Autoblinda 41* armoured car. Weight of the *L 6* was actually nearer seven tons, length 12 feet 7 inches (3.84 metres) and width and height 6 feet 1 inch (1.85 metres). A four-cylinder Fiat (SPA) engine of about 70 hp drove the vehicle at 28 mph (45 km/h). In all about 500 were produced; a version with a flame-thrower was not adopted.

The *L 6/40*, which was fitted with radio, first saw action with the reconnaissance group of the *CAM* at the end of 1941 when four were sent for service trials. The first formation to use the tank in quantity was the Third Group of the *Lancieri di Novara* regiment sent to North Africa as the armoured group of *Littorio* Armoured Division in the spring of 1942. Generally *L 6/40*s were issued to the reconnaissance formations of the Italian Army and saw service in Russia, for anti-partisan work in Yugoslavia (where some were captured and used against the Axis forces) and also in Sicily.

Possibly owing to shortage of turrets and 20-mm guns the later chassis were completed as *Semovente Da 47/32 Su Scafo L 40* – self-propelled anti-tank guns with the weapon mounted in an open-box superstructure. Estimates of numbers of these vary from 100 to 250. There was a radio-equipped platoon commander's vehicle and a company commander's vehicle with dummy guns. These *Semoventi* were perhaps first used in the Western Desert in 1942 but they were certainly later in action in Tunisia. After the Italian surrender the survivors were used by the *Wehrmacht* together with the original tanks. *L 6/40* light tanks remained in Italian service until well after the war.

Carro Armato L 3/35 Lf
Weight 3.4 tons (3.4 tonnes)
Crew two
Armament one FIAT-OCI flame-thrower with 520 litres fuel in trailer
Armour hull nose and driver's plate 13.5 mm, glacis 8.5 mm, sides and tail 8.5 mm, decking 6 mm, belly 6–13.5 mm.
Engine FIAT-SPA CV 3 four-cylinder inline liquid-cooled petrol, 43-hp
Speed 26 mph (42 km/h)
Range 75 miles (120 km)
Trench crossing 4 feet 10 inches (1.45 m)
Vertical step 2 feet 4 inches (70 cm)
Fording 2 feet 4 inches (70 cm)
Overall length 10 feet 5 inches (3.17 m)
Width 4 feet (1.4 m)
Height 4 feet 3 inches (1.29 cm)

Below: *An L 3/33 Lf and 3/35 Lf flame-thrower pictured without its fuel trailer. The obvious rivets on the superstructure of the top artwork mark this as the later model, the L 3/33 having a 'cleaner' appearance. The standard tankette mounted twin Fiat or Breda machine-guns in place of the long flame-thrower gun in the left of the superstructure front. These small and ineffectual vehicles were the main equipment of Italy's armoured forces in 1940 and reflected the general Italian weakness in mechanized warfare*

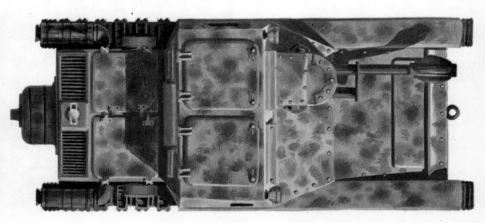

M 11/39 Medium Tank

The *M* 11/39 was a medium, break-through tank developed to complement the light *CV* series. When in 1933 it became clear that the new tankettes were not a complete replacement for the Fiat 3000, Fiat-Ansaldo designed a 12-ton Model 32 assault tank based on a scaled-up version of the tankette chassis. A Fiat 643N commercial diesel engine was fitted and the turretless vehicle mounted a short 45-mm gun in the hull front, with four machine-guns around the superstructure. This vehicle was not put into production but development work continued to a lighter, eight-ton design.

The new tank appeared in 1935 and mounted a 40-calibre Vickers Terni 37-mm gun in the right hull front. The weapon could be traversed 15 degrees left and right and 12 degrees up and down with hydraulic assistance in the horizontal plane. The gunner sat on the right and the driver slightly behind on the left, while there was a ten-sided turret with two 8-mm Breda machine-guns for the commander. The rear-mounted engine, still of commercial type, drove through a crash gear-box and the front sprockets. Steering was by epicyclic clutch and brake.

Trials showed that both the engine and suspension needed modification. Fiat therefore developed a new V8 diesel and Ansaldo a new suspension system utilizing on each side two semi-elliptically sprung assemblies of double-bogie wheel pairs. With the failure of the tankettes in Spain adding impetus to the programme, the eight-tonner was rebuilt to the new specifications in 1937. To ease eventual production a new, more rounded machine-gun turret was also adopted. Still designated *carro di rottura*, or, break-through tank, 100 were ordered.

Material shortages delayed production and it was not until 1939 that the tanks, now designated *Carri Armati M* 11/39 (*M* for *medio* – medium), began to be delivered. Weight had gone up during development and the production tanks had small detail modifications and, inexplicably, lacked the prototype's radio. A company of 12 took part in the summer manoeuvres when Italian blitzkrieg ideas were first tested but staff from Ansaldo manned the tanks, owing to lack of time to familiarize army crews. Further trials continued with the Third Tank Regiment and the balance of the order was not completed until well into 1940.

It was intended to use the tank as the main weapon of the armoured divisions. Each battalion would consist of 31 tanks, two companies, each of three four-tank platoons and a command vehicle, with an HQ company composed of a commander's tank and four replacements. The 32nd Tank Regiment of the *Ariete* began conversion, but events intervened and the best tanks available to Italy, 24 *M* 11/39s, were sent out in May 1940 as a *Compagnia Speciale Carri M* to bolster the Italian position in East Africa.

Once war had broken out in June requests soon came from North Africa for a better tank than the *L* 3, whose deficiencies had been shown up in the initial clashes with the British. Seventy *M* 11/39s were therefore put under the command of the Fourth Tank Regiment and arrived at Benghazi in July: First and Second Battalions were thus equipped and a separate company was joined with one of *L* 3s in a mixed battalion allocated to the *Maletti* Group, a typically heterogeneous Italian formation of motorized and unmotorized Libyan units. First and Second Battalions were each allocated to one of the groups of the new Libyan Tank Command when it was set up in August. Each group also contained three *L* 3 battalions.

In their first skirmishes with the British the *M* 11/39s were quite successful, usually used in a relatively dispersed infantry support role during the initial Italian advance into Egypt. Like the smaller *L* 3s, however, they suffered severely from breakdowns. By September, when the armoured groups were reformed the First Battalion was down from 31 to 9 serviceable tanks. Clashes with British armour also began to show up the *M* 11's weaknesses in both armament and protection. The 37-mm gun was an old and weak design and its location in the hull put the tank at a severe tactical disadvantage, while 30-mm frontal armour was no match for the British two-pounder (40-mm) anti-tank and tank gun or 14-mm side armour for the Boys anti-tank rifle.

With the opening of the British offensive in December, disaster struck. Second Battalion, two *M* 11 companies attached to *Maletti* Group, was surprised at Nibeiwa on the first day and all 22 of its tanks overrun. Although First Battalion was part of the new Special Armoured Brigade with an *M* 13 battalion and two more of *L* 3s, it could take little real part in the fighting because most of its tanks were marooned, unserviceable, in Tobruk. During the attack on this stronghold in January 1941 the Sixth Australian Divisional Cavalry Regiment used captured *M* 11/39s against their former owners. There were five of these tanks with large white kangaroos (the divisional sign) painted prominently on the turret, hull, front and sides for identification. Together with a later *M* 13/40 they equipped one squadron, Ringo, which operated with two others, Rabbit and Wombat, each of two *M* 13/40 tanks.

The defeat of the Italian Army saw the destruction or capture of almost every *M* 11/39 in the area. The vehicles in East Africa, after a brief moment of triumph in the conquest of British Somaliland in 1940, suffered a similar fate when Ethiopia fell the next year. Only a handful survived in Italy in training roles until 1943.

The *M* 11/39 symbolizes most of the weaknesses of the Italian armoured forces with its poor design, long period of development, production difficulties, unreliability and limited repair facilities. These were all reflections of Italy's limited reserves of raw materials and technological expertise which also discouraged the whole-hearted adoption of a more advanced armoured doctrine. The Italians were unprepared for the British blitzkrieg of December 1940, spearheaded by Matilda and Cruiser tanks far superior to the *M* 11/39. Even if more had been in working order the result could hardly have been different. To use a sporting metaphor: earlier in 1940 the First Division in armoured warfare had beaten the Second. Now the Second had smashed the Third.

Carro Armato M 11/39
Weight 10.8 tons (10.97 tonnes)
Crew three
Armament one 37-mm Vickers-Terni (L/40) gun
with 84 rounds and two 8-mm Breda Model 38
machine-guns with 2,800 rounds
Armour hull nose 30 mm, glacis 14 mm, driver's
plate 30 mm, sides 14–15 mm, decking 8 mm,
belly 10 mm, tail 14 mm; turret front 30 mm,
sides and rear 14 mm, top 7 mm
Engine one FIAT-SPA 8T V-8 liquid-cooled
diesel, 43-hp
Speed 21 mph (34 km/h)
Range 124 miles (200 km)
Trench crossing 6 feet 6 inches (2 m)
Vertical step 2 feet 7½ inches (80 cm)
Fording 3 feet 3 inches (1 m)
Overall length 15 feet 6½ inches (4.73 m)
Width 7 feet 2 inches (21.8 m)
Height 7 feet 4½ inches (2.25 m)

Top right: *The M 13/40. The M 11/39 was
developed into this much superior tank. The
similarity in design to the earlier tank is obvious.*
Bottom right: *The M 11/39*
Below: *Desolate and abandoned, this vehicle
typifies the fate of almost every M 11/39. It is one
of the 22 tanks which fell into British hands at
Nibeiwa in December 1940. An obsolete design at
birth the M 11/39 stood little chance against
vastly superior British types such as the Matilda.
Unreliability was added to inadequate armour and
and an armament which was both badly placed and
also weak*

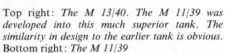

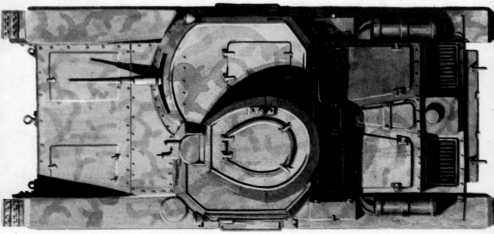

M 13/40 Series

From 1938 the possibilities were explored of mounting a more powerful gun on the *M* 11/39 chassis and after the invariable delays the first prototype of the *M* 13/40 appeared in early 1940 and 1,900 were ordered. The gun, a 32-calibre 47-mm weapon of adequate performance (muzzle velocity 2,060 fps or 630 m/s) was mounted in a revolving turret, a major design advance over the *M* 11/39. There was a co-axial Breda 8-mm machine-gun and after another could be mounted in the turret roof for AA purposes, firing through open hatches. Two more machine-guns were mounted in the right hull front. Although maximum hull armour remained unchanged from the *M* 11/39, all-round general protection was improved. The crew was increased to four: driver, machine-gunner, loader and commander/gunner. The internal layout and the commander's combination of functions was unfortunate as was the design of the turret itself, the slots in the fixed mantlet for the armament being very subject to bullet splash.

The tank was built from armoured plates bolted to a steel frame and it retained the engine, transmission and suspension of its predecessor. With the increase in weight this meant that, although paper performance figures were only slightly reduced, the tank tended to be sluggish, especially when extra appliqué armour and sandbags were added in the field. The armour also had an unfortunate tendency to crack when it was hit, a result of Italy's less advanced metallurgy.

In all, however, the *M* 13/40 was an adequate tank by the standards of 1940 and almost as good as the German *PzKpfw* III. Some 250 were built by the end of the year. As with the *M* 11/39 it was intended to use it as the basic tank of the armoured divisions, with regiments of three battalions each containing three companies of three platoons of five tanks. With command vehicles and replacements this came to 50.

Ariete's 32nd Regiment was the first to begin re-equipment but events forced the pace of deployment. Faced with the need to strengthen the forces in North Africa the 32nd's Third Battalion was sent on its own to Libya, where, although allocated to the Special Tank Brigade, it was kept under central army command. Deployed piecemeal the *M* 13/40s were rapidly outmanoeuvred in the major British counter-offensive in December 1940. Three more battalions were sent out but they could not retrieve the situation and, cut off by British armour at Beda Fomm, no fewer than 101 were destroyed or captured. A total of 112 fell into British hands in a usable condition during the campaign and they were used to equip the Sixth Royal Tank Regiment. When Rommel began his major offensive on 31st March it was Britain's turn to be outflanked and most of their Italian tanks had to be abandoned. The year 1941 saw *M* 13/40s in action in Greece (with a battalion of the *Centauro*) and Yugoslavia. The *Ariete* also brought more to North Africa and later, with the similarly equipped *Littorio*, fought with Rommel through his successes and failures of 1941–2.

As production continued the long mudguards were cut back (after about 150 tanks) and radios began to be fitted. After 800 *M* 13/40s a new version appeared, usually called the *M* 14/41.

To improve performance a new 125-hp SPA 15T diesel engine was fitted, boosting speed slightly and range to 175 miles (280 km). Better filters were fitted to the air and fuel systems for desert service and most had the long mudguards restored. The *M* 13/40 continued in production beside the *M* 14/41 into 1942 and some of the former were re-worked with the new engine and filters. *M* 14/41s reached the Western Desert by the summer of 1942 and equipped the tank units of the *Centauro* Division which fought in Tunisia during this period.

By this time the design was beginning to show its age. Although Rommel compared the *M* 13/40s gun favourably with those of his own *PzKpfw* IIIs still fitted with short 50-mm weapons (despite the lower velocity), the Italian tank's armour had become thin by contemporary standards. An attempt was made to modernize the design further and an improved *M* 15/42 was developed. A longer 40-calibre 47-mm gun was fitted and a new 15TB petrol engine to boost power to 192 bhp (in practice 170) and economize on Italy's dwindling reserves of diesel oil. To accommodate the new engine the hull was lengthened and the tank was slightly wider.

Opposite page, right: *The Semovente 75/18 assault gun based on the M 14/41 chassis*
Below: *An M 40 Semovente 75/18 assault gun group in action during the Battle of Alamein. Semoventi provided a cheap and more powerfully armed alternative to available Italian tanks and M 13/40 series chassis were increasingly diverted to their production from 1941*

Semovente da 75/18 Su Scafo M 41 (illustrated right)
Weight 13 tons (13.2 tonnes)
Armament one 75-mm Model 34 (L/18) gun
howitzer with 44 rounds
Armour superstructure front 25 + 25 mm, mantlet
50 mm, sides and rear 25 mm, top 9 mm
Engine one FIAT-SPA 15T, 125-hp
Height 6 feet 1 inch (1.85 m)
Other details as M 13/40 tank

Carro Armato M 13/40
Weight 13.5 tons (13.7 tonnes)
Crew four
Armament one 47-mm Model 37 (L/32) gun
with 104 (later 87) rounds and three 8-mm Breda
model 38 machine-guns with 3,048 rounds
Armour hull nose 30 mm, glacis 25 mm, driver's
plate 30 mm, sides 25 mm, decking 14 mm, belly
6 mm, tail 25 mm; turret front 40 mm, sides and
rear 25 mm, top 14 mm
Engine one FIAT-SPA 8T V-8 liquid-cooled diesel,
105-hp
Speed 19 mph (30 km/h)
Range 125 miles (200 km)
Trench crossing 6 feet 11 inches (2.1 m)
Vertical step 2 feet 11½ inches (90 cm)
Fording 3 feet 3 inches (1 m)
Overall length 16 feet 1½ inches (4.91 m)
Width 7 feet 4 inches (2.23 m)
Height 7 feet 10 inches (2.37 m)

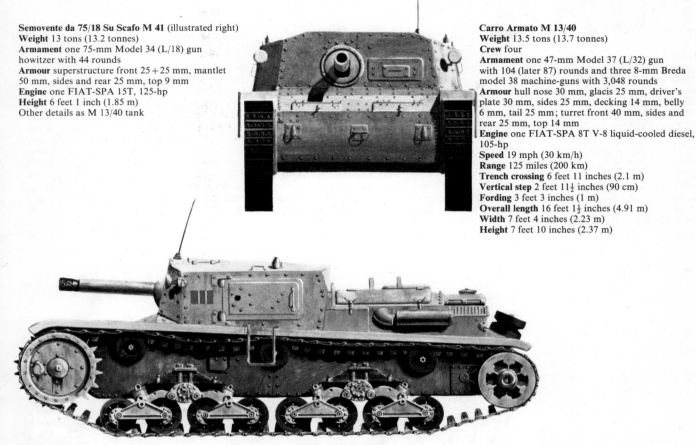

M 15/42s served with *Ariete* II Division in 1943 and continued with the post-war Italian army.

Only 82 were built owing to the decision in March 1943 to concentrate all medium-tank chassis production on *Semovente* assault guns. These had first been built in 1941 on the suggestion of Colonel Borlese of the artillery, basing his ideas on the successful use of German assault guns in the French campaign. Ansaldo demonstrated a mock-up on an *M* 13/40 chassis using the short 18-calibre 75-mm gun howitzer in a ball-mount at the front of a low superstructure armoured similarly to the tank. Thirty were ordered in January 1941 with the designation *Semovente da 75/18 su scafo M 40*. After successful trials with the prototype the order was doubled a month later. The *semovente* concept was simple but sound and well suited to Italian technical capabilities. After the initial orders were fulfilled 120 more were built, most using the new *M* 41 chassis. The tank was manned by a crew of three: driver, loader/radio operator and commander/gunner. These guns were used to equip artillery assault groups of, at first, two batteries of four guns each and later (1943) three batteries of six. *Semoventi* had come into service in North Africa with the *Ariete* the year before and with their powerful armament soon became an important part of Italy's armoured strength.

Each *Semovente* group had a number of command vehicles, usually four. These were developed from a prototype turretless *M* 13/40 converted in 1941. Production vehicles had range-finding equipment and two radios and were armed with twin 8-mm machine-guns with a third for AA use. In 1941 the *Carro Comando M* 41 was developed on the new *M* 14/41 chassis with a 13.2-mm Breda heavy machine-gun. Command vehicles were also eventually built on the *M* 15/42 chassis designated *M* 42 and some of these had longer-range radios for the control of aircraft. There was also an observation post version of the *M* 13/40 tank with dummy gun and rangefinder in the turret.

The *M* 42 chassis began to be used for *Semovente* production about the time that of tanks ceased and the assault guns were allocated to tank units. Initially the usual 75/18 was fitted, bringing numbers of such *Semoventi* to over 200, but two modifications were under development. The first was a new version of the chassis – lower, longer and wider. More heavily-armoured (50-mm) this *Semovente* mounted a version of the standard 105-mm gun howitzer developed by Ansaldo. The prototype appeared in January 1943 and eventually 454 were on order as the *Semovente da 105/25 su scafo M 43*. The first 30 of these impressive vehicles were delivered by the armistice and a group each was allocated to *Ariete* II and *Centauro* II. They were the most powerful Italian AFVs of the war.

The second was based on the normal *M* 42 chassis and involved the fitting of a longer gun. A 32-calibre 75-mm had been mounted experimentally on an early *M* 41 chassis and Ansaldo developed a new 34-calibre version, without muzzle brake, for the *Semovente*. Despite orders for 500, only one had been delivered by the time of surrender.

Two other self-propelled weapons produced by the Italians were open mountings on the rear of cut-down versions of tracked chassis. The more numerous was the 90-mm AA/AT gun on the *M* 14/41 chassis; 30 were built and saw service in North Africa in 1942–3. There was also a larger 149-mm model 1935 gun-howitzer on the *M* 43 chassis.

Following Italy's armistice with the Allies her armoured units were temporarily disbanded but two Blackshirt armoured groupings continued the battle for the *RSI* with various *M* 13/40 derivatives. *Semoventi* proved very popular with the Germans who adopted them in large numbers. Ansaldo produced for them in addition 55 of the *M* 42 75/18s as *Sturmgeschutz M 42 mit 75/18* (850)(i), 79 of the later type as *Sturmgeschutz M 42 mit 75/34* (851)(i) and 91 of the larger *Sturmgeschutz M 43 mit 105/25* (853)(i).

It had been planned by the Italians to produce a variant of the *M 43 Semovente* using the 76-mm AA gun and the Germans continued this, producing a *Sturmgeschutz M 43 mit 75/46* (852)(i), with a re-bored version of the gun fitted with a prominent counterweight. Thirteen of these were built from 1944 to 1945, together with eleven fitted with the shorter 34-calibre gun of the later *M 42s*, designated *Sturmgeschutz M 43 mit 75/34* (851)(i). *Semoventi* 75/18 were used after the war by Italian forces.

JAPAN

Japanese tanks were first developed for the support of the traditional infantry and cavalry arms: tankettes followed for logistic and communications purposes and, during the 1930s, light tanks for a more independent armoured role. These functions tended to merge as technological developments, operational utility and doctrinal conservatism overtook procurement intentions. Japanese use of armour was also conditioned by her theatres of operations. In the war against North America and Britain, from 1941 to 1945, tanks could usually only be transported and used in small groups. On the Asian mainland against China and Russia larger forces could be

exploited in a war of manoeuvre, but the differing sophistication of these two opponents affected Japanese equipment and ideas significantly.

At first Japan used British and French tanks for experiments at the infantry school and in 1925, when modernization of the army began, the first tank company was established. More vehicles were purchased from abroad for both use and experiment, including Renault FTs and later NCIs from France (designated KO-GATA SHENSA and OTSU-GATA SHENSA), Vickers 'Six-Tonners' and a Medium C from Britain. Japan also began development of an indigenous Number 1 Tank of ambitious specification to test

her own construction capabilities. The Army Technical Headquarters, which was a moving force behind this project, was to be a constant factor for progress in the development of Japanese armoured forces.

The lessons learned from this tank – which compared well with foreign tanks – were combined with those from the Medium C to produce a smaller vehicle for infantry support purposes. This appeared in 1929, 2589 in the Japanese calendar, hence the designation Type 89. It was the earliest Japanese tank produced in quantity and was used during 1932 in Japan's first major aggression against China. From the next year

tank regiments were formed, allocated to infantry divisions for direct support and these were later grouped into brigades.

It was at this time that the cavalry also acquired armour. Development of a Type 92 Combat Car, or light tank, was begun for the armoured company of each cavalry brigade in 1931. This was a small 3½ ton vehicle with a three-man crew. The armament consisted of two machine-guns, a 6.5-mm or 13.2-mm weapon mounted in the hull and a turret-mounted 6.5-mm. In the prototype the suspension consisted of two elliptically-sprung pairs of bogie wheels each side, but in production versions three pairs of wheels were adopted to improve cross-country mobility. Later still came four larger wheels with modified springing. Large numbers of these vehicles saw service with the cavalry brigades and cavalry scouting squadrons attached to infantry divisions.

With Japanese ambitions centred on the wide open spaces of Mongolia and Northern China a vehicle was needed for command and liaison

Left: A Type 95 light tank – one of the mainstays of Japanese armoured strength in World War II

roles and to keep open the supply lines to the widely-dispersed garrisons and armies. Small armoured tractors seemed to be the solution and the Carden Loyd tankette was purchased as a guide. The design was developed with a new suspension into the Type 94 Tankette, a small front-engined 2.65-ton vehicle with a 6.5-mm machine-gun turret. Although only armoured to 12 mm against small-arms fire it proved adequate against Chinese forces for infantry support and, manufactured in quantity, was allocated on the basis of one company per infantry division. New versions were later developed; a Type 94 Modified with improved suspension and the Type 97 with 37-mm gun and rear-mounted diesel engine used for infantry support.

The lighter, air-cooled diesel engine was the major progressive feature of Japanese armour at this period. Water was scarce in Mongolia, Manchuria and North China and the Japanese had been put off petrol by a serious fire in their imported British Medium C during tests. Diesel oil could be obtained in greater quantities than petrol from any given amount of crude oil and there were other advantages of less fuel loss during storage and increased range, all important to a country short of petroleum. A whole series of standardized diesel engines was developed and used in almost all Japanese AFV designs until 1945; they were also noted for the range of fuel grades that could be used.

The first new type of tank to be diesel-engined was the Type 95 designed for the new Independent Mixed Brigade. This progressive formation was first assembled under the influence of Western theory and practice in 1933. It was a combination of three type 89 companies and an infantry regiment, artillery regiment and engineer company, all motorized. The speeds of the various vehicles soon proved incompatible and a requirement was issued for a fast, light tank for the new brigade. The Japanese also began to develop specialized AFVs such as a fully-tracked Type 97 engineer vehicle carrying flame-throwers and a bridge span projected into place by rockets.

The Mixed Brigade was used to spearhead attacks in the full-scale war with China that broke out in 1937, but the lack of serious opposition prevented its potential from becoming apparent and it was eventually disbanded. However, armoured clashes with the Soviet Union, culminating in Zhukov's use of blitzkrieg methods to shatter Japanese forces at Khalkin Gol on the Mongolian/Manchurian border in 1939, emphasized the importance of modern armour and the deficiencies of Japanese technology, organization and ideas. Although Japanese tanks were not involved in the battle their performance was shown to be inadequate compared with the Soviet tanks and development of an up-gunned version of the latest Type 97 Medium began. In 1940 this defeat, coupled with the German victories in Europe, also led to the formation of two armoured divisions in Manchukuo around the tank brigades deployed there and the adoption of new battle manuals stressing

concentration and mobility. Each division had on paper a three-regiment tank brigade of Type 97 mediums and Type 95 lights. A third armoured division was later formed by fully mechanizing the cavalry units in Mongolia and, in 1943, this joined the other two in a Tank Army set up the previous year.

Japanese armour began the war successfully against the Allies in the Philippines and Malaya – Third Tank Brigade's vehicles proving particularly successful in the latter campaign in small, mixed combat groups containing ten to fifteen tanks each. It was partly due to the need for dispersed groups of armour in these campaigns, and in Burma and the Pacific Islands, that the tank divisions were rarely up to strength. One or more tank regiment was usually detached for independent use and there were always as many regiments independent as in the divisions. The Japanese, indeed, rarely displayed a full appreciation of the true nature of mechanized operations. One tank division was effectively used in China during the 1944 offensive in Honan but another, the Second, was frittered away uselessly the same year as a series of static pill-boxes during the fighting in the Philippines.

Japanese vehicles were, moreover, usually inferior to their opponents. It was not that new designs were neglected, many appeared – new battle tanks of increasing size, self-propelled guns and amphibious tanks. No fewer than 1,104 armoured personnel carriers were produced, the fully-tracked Type 1 HO-KI, half-tracked Type 1 HO-HA and amphibious KATSU-SHA. Few were deployed, however, as AFV production had to be subordinated to the more pressing air and naval needs of the maritime war of attrition. From 1944, American air raids also began to disrupt production. Spare parts became a real problem and many vehicles were lost for this reason. As for complete tanks, Japan had produced 1,976 tanks of all types during the 1930s, and 4,424 more were completed by 1945. Peak year was 1942 with 1,290 vehicles but production soon slumped to 750 in 1943, 295 in 1944 and 130 in 1945.

The Japanese high command, conditioned by easy victories against a largely unarmoured foe in China, preferred to keep old, standard and obsolete vehicles in production rather than re-equip. This made some sense given Japan's limited industrial capacity but good designs were delayed too long and when they, and new vehicles, became available, production facilities were not. What new vehicles there were, moreover, tended to be kept for home defence and did not see action in the combat theatres. The final *débâcle* came in August 1945 when Soviet forces, equipped with 5,500 modern AFVs, smashed the Japanese armies in Manchuria with their 1,250 obsolete machines. It was one of the most crushing blitzkriegs of the war.

After the war much Japanese armour fell into the hands of the Chinese Communists and the Viet Minh who used them in action in Korea and also in Indo-China.

Type 89 Medium Tank

The design of this infantry support vehicle dated back to the Number 1 Tank project begun in 1925; its specification had stressed good all-round performance as it was essentially a demonstration of technology rather than an answer to an operational requirement. In order to attack strong enemy defences a 57-mm gun with two subsidiary machine-gun turrets was demanded, together with armour to resist contemporary 37-mm anti-tank guns. Specified performance was 15½ mph (25 km/h), that of the standard army truck, to simplify movement problems. Weight was to be around 15 tons.

Despite problems with the production of armour plate and other technical difficulties the vehicle eventually emerged as an unarmoured prototype. Weight had increased to 18 tons and this was felt by the high command to be too extravagant for the infantry support role. A smaller 10-ton, 37-mm armed light tank was, therefore requested similar to the British Vickers Medium C purchased in 1927. The design of Number 1 was scaled down and a new prototype appeared from the Osaka Arsenal in 1929. Development of the heavy tank continued but it never went into production.

The new light tank mounted a similar 57-mm gun to that in the Number 1. A 6.5-mm machine-gun was mounted in the turret rear (a rather idiosyncratic Japanese feature), and in the left hull front. Instead of Number 1's 140-hp V8, a 105-hp Mitsubishi copy of a six-cylinder Daimler engine was fitted driving through the rear sprocket to give similar performance figures to the earlier tank. Steering was on the clutch and brake principle developed for the Number 1 and the suspension was a simplified and scaled-down version of the larger vehicle's. Instead of 19 bogie wheels each side the new tank had nine, two double-sets of leaf-sprung bogie wheel pairs with an independently sprung wheel at the front. Armoured skirting protected the springs.

With the official designation Type 89, from the Japanese year of introduction, the tank was put into production at the new tank arsenal built by Mitsubishi. With a new larger symmetrical turret the weight rose to 11½ tons and the erstwhile light tank became a medium, acquiring the name CHI-RO from the abbreviated form of the Japanese word *chugata*, meaning medium. Together with the new OTSU-GATA SENSHA tanks purchased from France, Type 89 Mediums were used in the Shanghai incident of 1932 as part of the naval landing force. Despite the unsuitable terrain the Japanese tanks with their stouter suspensions, superior mobility and greater reliability proved more popular in supporting the infantry assaults on the Chinese defensive positions. With no powerful anti-tank guns to worry about, the Type 89's inferior armour protection of 17-mm (as opposed to 30-mm) was not unduly important.

In 1933 three infantry support regiments of Type 89s were formed, each of two companies of ten. Two were stationed in Japan and one in Manchukuo at Kungchuling. Here, the next year, three more companies were formed into a Fourth Regiment as part of the Independent Mixed Brigade. Despite its designed role, the 89

had a moderate range and its mechanical robustness lent itself to mobile operations against ill-equipped opponents. This had been shown when a mixed company of Type 89s and Type 92 Combat Cars had led the long-distance campaign into Jehol in 1933.

In 1934 a major modification occurred with the appearance of the Type 89B (89-KO) with the new Mitsubishi-designed diesel engine. Petrol-engined tanks now became Type 89A (89-OTSU). After extensive field trials in Northern Manchukuo the 89B was adopted and produced by Mitsubishi and the other tank factories that Japan was building up both in the home islands and Manchukuo.

As production continued at the various plants, so external modifications took place. The original turret cupola, which hinged open as a unit, was replaced by one with opening hatches, an improved external mantlet for the gun was adopted and the machine-guns were protected by armoured sleeves. The original girder mounting five return rollers was replaced by a new arrangement with four rollers and a new design of armoured skirting. Most vehicles, either with or without the other modifications, had a new sloping frontal plate replacing the original one with its more vulnerable vertical top. With the new arrangement, the driver's and machine-gunner's positions were sometimes reversed. Western intelligence called the sloping front combined with the older features the Type 92 and those with the newer trackwork the Type 94 but these were not Japanese designations. Unditching tails, to improve cross-country performance, and new tracks, to boost speed, were later fitted.

Type 89s, in their various forms, took a prominent part in the battles of Japan's war with China in 1937, again demonstrating their cross-country capacity, for example in the mud along the Peking–Hankow railway. They fought the Russians in 1938 and, although being replaced by the Type 97, formed part of the equipment of the two tank regiments that helped conquer the Philippines during 1941 and 1942. Type 89Bs also played a part in the conquest of Burma.

By this time the tank was obsolete in world terms. Its gun was short, weak (1,148 fps or 350 m/s muzzle velocity) and only had a high explosive capability. Armour was thin, particularly for a primarily infantry support vehicle. The Type 89 could, however, carry out the World War I function of dealing with machine-guns and barbed wire and its robustness stood it in good stead in both the wide open spaces of China and the jungles of the Philippines and Burma. It was a useful infantry support tank – as long as the opposition was badly equipped.

Top right: A late Type 89B with crew. This obsolete tank was still being encountered in the Philippines in 1944
Far right: A Type 89A – note the early cupola, driver's plate and suspension skirting
Right: A late Type 89B advances over a Chinese bridge repaired by engineers. This tinted photograph shows the multi-coloured camouflage typical of Japanese armour. The unditching tail and later cupola are also illustrated

Type 89B CHI-RO
Weight 12.8 tons
Crew four
Armament one 57-mm Type 90 gun with 100
rounds and two 6.5-mm Type 91 machine-guns
with 2,745 rounds
Armour hull front, sides and rear 17 mm, decking
10 mm; turret front 17 mm, sides and rear 15 mm,
top 10 mm
Engine one Mitsubishi inline six-cylinder air-
cooled diesel, 115-hp
Speed 15.5 mph (25 km/h)
Range 100 miles (160 km)
Trench crossing 8 feet 1½ inches (2.5 m)
Vertical step 2 feet 7½ inches (80 cm)
Fording 3 feet 3 inches (1 m)
Overall length 18 feet 10½ inches (5.75 m) with
tail
Width 7 feet 2 inches (2.18 m)
Height 8 feet 5 inches (2.56 m)

Type 95 Light Series

The Type 89 Medium was too slow for convenient operation with the wheeled transport of the mechanized brigade and in 1933 development of a new, faster tank was begun. It was to be a light tank of only seven tons and armoured only against small-arms fire as the high command considered this sufficient for the task. The suspension was based on that of the new Type 94 tankette with two pairs of bogie wheels each side-mounted on bell cranks and supported by compressed horizontal, helical springs. This principle was to become standard for most subsequent Japanese tanks. The new diesel engine was fitted in the rear, driving through the front sprockets. Standard clutch and brake steering was employed and the crew consisted of a driver, a machine-gunner working a hull-mounted weapon and a commander/gunner with a turret-mounted 37-mm gun.

Mitsubishi completed the prototype in 1934 and it was sent for trials with both cavalry and infantry. The latter were not impressed by either its armament or protection but, after operational trials with the Independent Mixed Brigade in Manchukuo, a production order was given. A second prototype was constructed in 1935 (with two return rollers instead of one) and the vehicle was adopted as the Type 95 Light Tank, with a widened fighting compartment.

The Type 95 was produced in large quantities for a Japanese tank: 1,164 at the Mitsubishi tank arsenal (who gave it its most widely used name HA-GO) and the rest, out of a total of approximately 1,300, at smaller plants. The cavalry had earlier shown interest in the design as a gun-armed replacement for the Type 92 Combat Car, and the HA-GO was procured for the cavalry brigades and units attached to infantry formations. The Independent Mixed Brigade adopted the HA-GO and used it during the opening offensive in China in 1937. Opposition was not great and neither the formation nor the tank had an opportunity to prove itself. Despite, or perhaps because of, this combat experience, the reluctance of the infantry to adopt the Type 95 was overcome and it was taken into the Tank Regiments, equipping one ten-tank company (three platoons of three with commander), others being attached to HQ vehicles. Unfortunately, and surprisingly, given its armoured brigade role, radio had not been a requirement and few commanders' vehicles were so fitted.

The HA-GO appeared on every front on which Japanese forces were engaged and had some success particularly in Malaya, although where any well-handled anti-tank guns were encountered, the odds were firmly against it. As usual with Japanese armour, the design, conceived when the only opposition was the ill-equipped Chinese Army, had its major strengths in mechanical robustness and mobility (its cross-country speed was as high as 20 mph or 32 km/h), rather than in armour or firepower. Although production vehicles had an improved gun of 2,214 fps (675 m/s) velocity (as against 1,886 fps or 575 m/s) this was over 300 fps (91 m/s) less than its American counterpart. Moreover the limited depression of the main armament – which left a dead zone of almost eight

yards' radius around the tank – compounded the commander/gunner's problem of preventing stalking, particularly in close country, while also trying to attend to the guns and command the tank. By the time production ceased in 1943 the HA-GO was obsolete and many finished their days as not particularly effective dug-in pillboxes on such beaches as Iwo Jima.

Various improvements to the basic Type 95 were carried out. After experiments with the original prototype, units in North Manchukuo had their tanks fitted with a modified suspension with a small extra road wheel between each normal pair, mounted on inverted cranks. This was to improve performance over fields of kaoliang corn, the basic crop of the area. Although the original fitting was combined with modified springing, the improvement could be applied to the standard unit of any tank deployed in the area. Latterly, attempts were made to up-gun the HA-GO, as the Type 3 KE-RI, with a short 57-mm model 97 gun made available by the up-gunning of the CHI-HA Medium. Owing to the confined space in the turret this conversion was not successful and when the larger 47-mm turret of the SHINHOTO CHI-HA became available the entire fitting was applied to the Type 95 to

become the Type 4 KE-NU with a four-man crew. By this stage of the war, however, few could be produced.

Amphibious tanks had been experimented with for some time but the only one to see widespread service was based on the HA-GO. Appearing as the Type 2 KA-MI in 1942 it had a larger hull for greater buoyancy with an extra crew member carried as a mechanic to supervise the power take-offs to the two propellers and bilge pump. Two detachable pontoons were carried fore and aft for flotation, the latter with two rudders for steering in water. Armour was as on the HA-GO but the gun was a later version and a co-axial machine gun was fitted. By the time the KA-MI was deployed with naval and marine units the days of Japan's maritime offensive were largely over, although it was used for small-scale counter-attacks in the Marshalls and Marianas.

An improved light tank with transversely mounted supercharged engine was developed, the Type 98 KE-NI, lighter and faster (31 mph) with 16-mm armour and a new Type 0 37-mm gun (2,493 fps or 760 m/s muzzle velocity). After experiments with a four-wheeled Christie-type suspension, the alternative was adopted – a modified version of the standard system with

three cranked wheel pairs each side. Owing to the high command's policy of standardization, the tank was belatedly put into production in 1942 and only 200 were made. An improved Type 2 KE-TO with roomier turret and Type 1 37-mm gun (2,625 fps or 800 m/s) was delayed until 1944 and produced in still smaller quantities; a completely new Type 5 KE-HO with 20-mm armour and 47-mm gun, although designed in 1942, did not get beyond the prototype stage. Although these designs attest to the energy of the Army Technical Headquarters, the need might well be questioned for new manifestations of what was, by this time, an outdated concept. After the war, China continued to use the Type 98 and some may have seen service in Korea.

Right: This HA-GO is pictured in a typical Japanese camouflage scheme. A version of the Japanese flag often appeared as national marking on tanks. The usual Japanese suspension, of bell cranks and horizontal springs, is clearly seen in the side view
Below: The Type 95 CHI-HA saw large-scale service in World War II. Tanks of this type were attached to infantry and cavalry formations as well as forming an important part of tank units

Type 95 HA-GO
Weight 7.5 tons
Crew three
Armament one 37-mm Type 94 gun with 119 rounds and two 7.7-mm Type 97 machine-guns with 2,940 rounds
Armour hull nose 12 mm, glacis 9 mm, driver's plate 12 mm, sides 12 mm, decking and belly 9 mm, tail 6–12 mm; turret front, sides and rear, 12 mm, top 9 mm
Engine one Mitsubishi inline six-cylinder air-cooled diesel, 110-hp
Speed 28 mph (45 km/h)
Range 155 miles (250 km)
Trench crossing 6 feet 7 inches (2 m)
Vertical step 2 feet 8 inches (80 cm)
Fording 3 feet 3 inches (1 m)
Overall length 14 feet 4½ inches (4.38 m)
Width 6 feet 9 inches (2.06 m)
Height 7 feet 10 inches (2.39 m)

Type 97 Medium Series

The stimulus to develop a new medium tank came, as in the case of most other Japanese tanks, from the technical rather than the operational branch of the Japanese Army's command structure. Army Technical Headquarters saw that the Type 89 was increasingly inferior to European tanks being slow, under-gunned and under-armoured. It was also felt that a new, fast medium should be developed for the Independent Mixed Brigade rather than a light tank and two designs were initiated, a 13.5-ton First Plan from Mitsubishi and a 10-ton Second Plan from Osaka Arsenal. Both prototypes appeared in 1937 as the CHI-HA and CHI-NI respectively and, although the Operations Department preferred the latter, which only had a one-man turret and was therefore cheaper, the outbreak of the China incident downgraded considerations of economy, and led to the adoption of the larger design for service use.

Two prototype CHI-HAs appeared, one with interleaved wheels, and the other employing a version of the standard suspension of the Type 94 tankette and Type 95 Light with three pairs of large, double bogie wheels each side connected by middle-mounted bell cranks horizontally sprung against each other. To improve cross-country performance the production vehicles adopted a modification of this suspension for the centre pairs only, the front and back wheels being independently sprung. Construction was by welding and riveting and the armour was well shaped. A small turret was mounted to the right of the hull. Its firepower was disappointing, being a new Type 97 version of the old short 57-mm gun. This did fire an armour-piercing round, but only at 1,378 fps (420 m/s) – half the velocity of the later British six-pounder (57-mm) of similar calibre. Unlike that of the CHI-NI the turret was two-man so the tank commander did not have to double as gunner, and the ring was large enough to allow later up-gunning. Machine-guns in armoured sleeves were in the hull front and turret rear with a third sometimes fitted for AA use. A powerful new engine of standard pattern drove through the front sprockets and steering was by normal clutch and brake.

The CHI-HA compared favourably with its contemporaries in all except gun power and this deficiency became apparent when the Soviet Army showed the Japanese the nature of modern armoured opposition in 1938–9. Development, therefore, began of a larger turret, mounting a high-velocity armament based on the standard 47-mm anti-tank weapon. The new 48-calibre Type 1 tank gun had a muzzle velocity of 2,625 fps (800 m/s) which compared satisfactorily with foreign weapons such as the contemporary *PzKpfw* III's 2,240 fps (684 m/s) 42-calibre 50-mm. The programme was delayed, however, by renewed complacency and the new SHINHOTO (New Turret) CHI-HA only began to enter service in 1942. By this time it was already becoming obsolete particularly in terms of its armour protection which was only slightly improved on the hull sides. Again, the new turret was set towards the right and had a machine-gun in the rear.

By this time the standard CHI-HA had equipped some independent tank regiments and those

in the armoured divisions. It had seen service in China and Malaya where individual tank companies were handled daringly in co-operation with infantry and engineers to break the British defences at Jitra and on the Slim River. They then spearheaded the swift advance down the peninsula which followed.

In a Japanese tank regiment the Type 97 provided the three or four medium companies, each of three platoons of three with a company commander. More were attached to Regimental HQ, one or more of these sometimes being the SHI-KI command vehicle with extra communications and vision equipment and an additional 37-mm or 57-mm gun in place of the machine-gun in the hull front. There was also a commander's SHINHOTO CHI-HA with a dummy gun. Most CHI-HAs had radio fitted to help tactical co-ordination with a prominent curved aerial in the original tanks being mounted around the top of the turret front. There were various specialized variants. In 1942 three self-propelled guns (gun tanks) appeared on the Type 97 chassis, perhaps stimulated by the successful assault gun designs of Japan's Axis allies. The HO-NI I mounted a modern 75-mm high-velocity gun, the HO-NI II, a shorter 105-mm weapon and the HO-RO, an old 150-mm howitzer. These were mounted in open shields, armoured frontally to the same thickness as the tank, and they proved useful in providing extra firepower in the final defensive battles. A few original CHI-HAs were converted to flail mine-

clearers, flamethrower tanks and bridgelayers while some SHINHOTO CHI-HAs became bull-dozer tanks. There was also a SE-RI recovery vehicle on the Type 97 chassis with rear crane jib and small machine-gun turret.

The SHINHOTO CHI-HA, to which standard many older vehicles were converted, was the only new tank to see large-scale service in the period after 1942. A 17-ton Type 1 CHI-HE with the 47-mm gun in a revised turret, a slightly better-shaped welded hull armoured to 50-mm, and a 240-hp engine was put into limited production in 1941. A Type 2 HO-I gun tank with a short 75-mm gun in a revolving turret was adopted for its support the next year, but, although some of both these types saw action, few were produced.

The appearance of larger Allied tanks with 75-mm guns led to experiments with the Type 95 75-mm field gun to improve the Japanese medium tank's firepower. Eventually a version of the higher-velocity Type 90 weapon was adopted and fitted in an enlarged turret on the CHI-HE chassis as the Type 3 CHI-NU. The gun was a 38-calibre weapon and had a muzzle velocity of 2,231 fps (680 m/s) which put it in terms of performance between that of the British and American tank guns of similar calibre. The 18.5-ton tank, if something of an improvization, was almost of American Sherman standard, but it suffered from production problems and only saw service in limited numbers from 1944. The same gun was also mounted in an enclosed

Type 97 SHINHOTO CHI-HA
Weight 15.6 tons
Crew five
Armament one 47-mm Type 1 (L/48) gun with 104 rounds and two 7.7-mm Type 97 machine-guns with 2,575 rounds
Armour hull nose 15 mm, glacis 17 mm, driver's plate 25 mm, sides 20–35 mm, decking 10 mm, belly 8 mm, tail 20 mm; turret front 25 mm, mantlet 30 mm, sides and rear 25 mm, top 10 mm
Engine one Mitsubishi V-12 air-cooled diesel, 170-hp
Speed 24 mph (38 km/h)
Range 130.5 miles (210 km)
Trench crossing 8 feet 1½ inches (2.5 m)
Vertical step 3 feet (91 cm)
Fording 3 feet 3 inches (1 m)
Overall length 18 feet 1 inch (5.5 m)
Width 7 feet 8 inches (2.33 m)
Height 7 feet 11 inches (2.38 m)

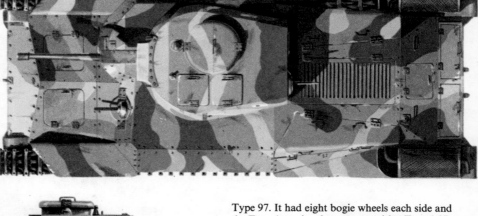

Right: *The SHINHOTO CHI-HA was the most important Japanese medium tank of the war. Known as the 'Type 97 Special' to the Americans it could barely hold its own against the Sherman, and was totally outclassed by Soviet armour in 1945. Note the machine-gun mounted in the turret rear, and also the lengthened version of the standard Japanese suspension with centre-mounted bell cranks on the middle wheel pairs. The novel camouflage scheme was a Japanese standard*
Below: *An original CHI-HA of the Third Company, Seventh Tank Regiment advances in Bataan during the conquest of the Philippines – the Japanese were adept at using tanks in difficult conditions*

central superstructure on the Type 97 chassis as the HO-NI III gun tank.

A scaled-up 30-ton Type 4 CHI-TO with 75-mm armour retained the same suspension principles as its predecessors but had seven wheels each side as opposed to six and a 400 bhp engine. A new 38-calibre 75-mm gun, based this time on the Type 88 AA weapon, was fitted but its muzzle velocity was little improved at 2,362 fps (703 m/s), less than the German 43-calibre 75-mm tank gun. The six tanks of this type that were produced were left in Japan for home defence.

All these tanks were diesel-powered but the final Japanese design was fitted with a German-designed 550-hp BMW petrol engine in an attempt to bypass shortages of the standard diesel engines and speed production. This 37-ton Type 5 CHI-RI was the final extrapolation of the

Type 97. It had eight bogie wheels each side and the Type 4 gun in a large turret with a Type 1 37-mm in the hull. Armour was the same as the Type 4. However, it appeared only as a prototype.

As with the Type 98, such a plethora of new designs was hardly necessary and only complicated a production system that was already grinding to a halt. Once the Type 3 had been developed, a vehicle of moderate size and adequate fire-power, it might well have been standardized without going on to the larger tanks of 30 tons or more that unnecessarily confused the situation.

Experiments went on in other fields too, although few results saw service. Prototype KA-TO and HO-RI heavy self-propelled guns, on the CHI-RI chassis, were produced just before the war's end. Earlier, an amphibious tank had been produced on the CHI-HE chassis and some were used in action. This 26-ton Type 3 KA-CHI (which weighed almost 29 tons with pontoons) had a large box-type superstructure on which was mounted a turret with a Type 1 47-mm gun. A later Type 5 TO-KU was lower and mounted the 47-mm in the hull. A 25-mm automatic cannon was in the turret.

Despite all this activity it was still the SHIN-HOTO CHI-HA which met the Americans from Saipan to the Philippines and had to fight Soviet armoured forces when they mounted their offensive in August 1945. Its gun could just defeat the American Sherman but 25-mm armour was no protection from even the smallest enemy anti-tank gun. It stood no chance at all against a Soviet T-34/85. After the war the SHINHOTO CHI-HA saw considerable service with the People's Republic of China.

Black and white photographs

Blitz: Pages 6-7, 14, 16, 17, 18, 22 bottom, 30-31, 33, 35, 37 top; Fujiphotos: Pages 62-63; Keystone: Page 39; Imperial War Museum: Pages 56-57, 60-61; H. Le Masson: Page 19; RAC Tank Museum, Bovington: Pages 4-5, 6, 8, 10, 22 top, 27, 34, 44, 46, 47, 52-53, 53, 58-59 top, 59; Zennaro, Rome: Pages 48-49, 50, 54.

Colour photographs

Allied Archives: Pages 20-21; Bibliothèque Nationale/ Dorka: Pages 58-59; Imperial War Museum: Page 37 bottom; Signal / Nicole Marchand: Page 11; Staatsbibliothek, Berlin: Pages 8-9; US Army: Pages 40, 43